CATHOLIC CHURCHMEN
IN SCIENCE

Catholic Churchmen in Science

[SECOND SERIES]

SKETCHES OF THE LIVES OF CATHOLIC
ECCLESIASTICS WHO WERE AMONG
THE GREAT FOUNDERS IN SCIENCE

BY

JAMES JOSEPH WALSH

Essay Index Reprint Series

BOOKS FOR LIBRARIES PRESS
FREEPORT, NEW YORK

First Published 1909
Reprinted 1969

STANDARD BOOK NUMBER:
8369-1387-6

LIBRARY OF CONGRESS CATALOG CARD NUMBER:
67-22126

PRINTED IN THE UNITED STATES OF AMERICA

To
MY FATHER
TO WHOSE INTEREST IN WHAT IS BEST IN LIFE
I OWE ALL

PREFACE.

THIS second series of *Catholic Churchmen in Science* is another contribution to the important question of the relations of Faith and Science. Many even well-informed people seem to think that science and faith are incompatible, and that the more science a man knows the less faith he has, while the more he bows in submission to Faith in the things that are not seen, the less possibility is there of his doing good work in science or even of appreciating its true significance. In the abstract the question may seem difficult enough to decide. In the concrete it is a perfectly simple matter to find out what was the attitude of the great scientists of all ages toward Faith. A most important part of the answer to this question is contained in the lives of the ecclesiastics of the Roman Catholic Church who have achieved distinction in science. There are a good many Catholic churchmen whose original scientific work has stamped their names indelibly on the history of science in every century. From their lives it can be readily seen that men may be devout believers in all the mysteries of religion and yet do magnificent experimental work; they may submit their intellects humbly to Faith, yet have perfectly open minds that enable them to put searching ques-

tions to nature so as to make great advances in
science. This is just what is supposed to be impossible. Submission to authority in intellectual
matters of any kind is said to be fatal to the
faculty for investigation and inquiry that is so
important for progress in science. These lives
show that it is perfectly possible for a man to
accept revelation on authority and yet refuse to
believe anything relating to physical science except on demonstration.

Perhaps even more surprising than this for
most people will be the fact that these sketches
show that Catholic churchmen have been among
the greatest workers in science during the past
seven centuries. This surprise will be mitigated,
however, for those who realize that, quite contrary to the usual impression in English-speaking
countries, devout Catholics have at all times been
among the greatest scientific discoverers. Even
in what is usually supposed to be so unorthodox
a science as medicine, the majority of the greatest discoverers even in the nineteenth century
were, as I have shown in *Makers of Modern
Medicine,* among the most faithful adherents of
the Catholic Church. The tradition that the
Church is opposed to science is founded entirely
on ignorance of the true history of science.
When the Popes were paramount in education
during the centuries before the so-called Reformation, physical science flourished to a much
greater degree than is now thought. There were
then a dozen medical schools in Italy, the great-

est of them in the Papal States, and, as I have
shown in *The Popes and Science,* the Popes were
as devoted patrons of science as they were of
art and of architecture.

Most of the second series of sketches of Catholic churchmen have appeared in various periodicals during the past few years. My thanks are
here given to *The Ecclesiastical Review, The
American Catholic Quarterly, The Ave Maria,
St. John's Quarterly,* and *The Month* (London),
for permission to republish papers which appeared in their pages and which are here republished after careful revision and many additions.
The article on Guy De Chauliac formed the basis
of a lecture before the Johns Hopkins Historical
Club on Old-Time Medical Education. A large
portion of the article on Pope John XXI, the
Ophthalmologist Pope, appeared in *Ophthalmology,* a quarterly journal of ophthalmic science.

While the book has been in preparation I have
felt that a third volume of Catholic Churchmen
in Science is needed to complete, even in an imperfect way, the story of what they did for science. This should include sketches of the medieval monastic scientists, Roger Bacon, Cardinal
Nicholas of Cusa, Father Pazzi the astronomer,
and of some modern clergymen who have done
good work in the biological sciences. This I
hope to publish as soon as leisure will permit.

CONTENTS.

(xi)

I.
INTRODUCTION.

EVERY earnest glance we give to the realities around us, with intent to learn, proceeds from a holy impulse, and is really a song of praise. What difference can it make whether it take the shape of exhortation, or of passionate exclamation, or of scientific statement. These are forms merely. Through them we express, at least, the fact that God has done thus or thus.—EMERSON.

SCIENTIFIC investigation should be inspired by a purpose as animating to the general sympathy as was the religious zeal which built the Cathedral of Cologne or the Basilica of St. Peter.—AGASSIZ.

EVERY formula which expresses a law of nature is a hymn of praise to God.—MARIA MITCHELL.

HOW great is God, Ozanam, how great is God, and how our knowledge is naught.—AMPÈRE.

I.

INTRODUCTION.

IN this second series of *Catholic Churchmen
in Science* the purpose of the first series is
carried out more fully, and the argument there
outlined from the lives of great pioneer workers
in science who were Catholic ecclesiastics is continued to an ampler conclusion. The best possible answer to the contentions so often heard
that the Catholic Church is opposed to science,
is to be found in the lives of the many prominent churchmen who were also distinguished scientists, and of the great scientists who became
churchmen yet still continued their devotion to
science. In the first series, beginning with Copernicus and Basil Valentine in the fifteenth
century, the life of one or more of the great
pioneers in science in each subsequent century
was sketched. There was Linacre, the great
physician and scholar to whom English medicine owes so much, who " for his soul's sake "
became a priest in the early part of the sixteenth century, just when, if we would believe
many writers, the Church needed so much to be
reformed. There was Kircher, the great Jesuit
scientist, who was invited to Rome the year
after Galileo's trial in the seventeenth century
and who was the author of text-books in every

3

branch of physical science. These works were not conventional résumés of the science of the time, but contained original observations of great value in nearly every department of physics as well as great fundamental truths in medicine, especially regarding the bacterial cause of disease. It was indeed in respect of disease-distribution by various living agents, as fleas, flies, and mosquitoes, that this great Jesuit scientist of three centuries ago anticipated some of our most modern ideas.

In the same seventeenth century there was Steno or Stensen, one of the greatest anatomists of all times, and the acknowledged Father of Geology, born in Denmark and educated outside the Church, but becoming a Catholic after having closely studied the Church and her work for many years in Italy, and then a priest, and finally a bishop, in order that he might help in the conversion of his countrymen. In the eighteenth century there was the Abbé Haüy the great father of crystallography; while in the nineteenth century there was Abbot Mendel, whose name has been in all the biological periodicals in recent years, and whose fame is in all the laboratories of biological science in every country in Europe, in America, and even in distant Japan. Mendel's work was accomplished quietly in his monastery garden, but was interrupted because his fellow-monks thought so much of his piety and goodness of heart that they elected him Abbot of the Monastery, and then he devoted himself to directing and fostering and studying men, so as to make them ripe for heaven instead of studying further his plants and the great laws that he had established in the plant kingdom.

The whole round of physical science was represented in the previous series. There is no greater name in astronomy than that of Copernicus and no name of greater importance at the beginnings of chemistry than that of Basil Valentine. The biological sciences are often supposed to flourish in a field of human knowledge that is especially dangerous for religious orthodoxy, yet more of the great Catholic churchmen who were pioneers in the science worked in this department than in any other. Linacre, Kircher, Steno, and Mendel represent work in medical and scientific education and great discoveries in the biological sciences. In recent years geology has been supposed to be unorthodox in its tendencies; yet the great foundation-stone of modern geology was laid by Bishop Steno, after his conversion to the Catholic Church and at a time when he was on terms of the most intimate relationship with Catholic ecclesiastics in Italy. Physics, as represented by the work of Abbé Haüy in crystallography and of Kircher and his text-books, was not neglected.

In this second series, though once more examples of great original workers in science who were Catholic clergymen are taken from every century from the thirteenth to the nineteenth,

most attention is devoted to the earlier centuries.
Four of the men whose lives are sketched died
before the fifteenth century was much more
than half completed. As the Middle Ages are
often said to end with the fall of Constantinople
about this time, more than two-thirds of the
book is taken up with medieval scientists. This
large share of attention to these earlier times is
deliberate. It is often said that the thirteenth,
fourteenth, and fifteenth centuries have no scientific progress in them, because at this time the
Church was supreme in all matters of education;
and as it was her policy to discourage scientific
knowledge, lest it should interfere with faith,
therefore there is no history of science until after
the so-called Reformation. Those who still continue to believe that there was no science in the
Middle Ages either wilfully blind themselves
to a whole series of important facts in human
history or else they are allowing themselves to
be led into ignorance by men who have a definite
purpose in ignoring the great scientific work of
these centuries, which saw the foundation of the
Universities and the organization of teaching
along lines that have never been much disturbed
and certainly not departed from, despite all our
vaunted progress in education.

As a matter of fact the Universities during
the first three centuries of their existence were
based on the idea that science in our modern
acceptation of that term was by far the most
important factor in education. It was not until

after the Renaissance that the study of the
classics and of literature began to form the basis
of undergraduate teaching at the Universities
and to constitute the elements with which the
foundation of education was laid. Before that,
as was pointed out by Prof. Huxley in his inaugural address as the Rector of Aberdeen
University, "The scholars studied Grammar,
Rhetoric, Logic, Arithmetic and Geometry, Astronomy, Theology and Music. Their studies
contained in embryo at least what we now call
Philosophy, Mathematical and Physical Science
and Art." The whole quotation will be found
a little later in the sketch of Albertus Magnus,
and it brings out very clearly that these Universities were much more concerned with science
than with other studies. Besides, if further
proof of this were needed, the fact that everyone
of these Universities had a medical department
and that all these medical departments were
integral portions of the University, requiring
proper preparation in the undergraduate department before a student was allowed to enter upon
the study of medicine, and then prescribing four
or sometimes even five years of medical studies
before the degree of doctor was given, shows
how seriously science and scientific education
were taken at this time. Practically all the modern sciences, even astronomy, because of the
supposed influence of the stars on human con-
stitutions, were studied in these medical schools
and with comparatively quite as much success
as in the modern time,

The lives of the four men who have been chosen as types of Catholic churchmen who did great original work in science in the Middle Ages, constitute the best possible rebuttal of the objections to the Catholic Church founded on the presumed barrenness of these ages in science because of supposed Church opposition to this phase of education. Albertus Magnus is the only scholar in history to whose name has become irrevocably attached the epithet Great. Most of the men who are great in history have the epithet because of the harm their prowess as warriors did to mankind. Albert alone has the title because of the extent of his knowledge and because of the admiration of his own and succeeding generations for his wonderful intellectual capacity. He stands besides Aristotle as one of the two or three men who came the nearest to success in absorbing all the knowledge of their times. He knew much less than we do, because there has been an accumulation of knowledge since his time; but it is surprising in how many ways he anticipated modern knowledge and how near he came to the heart of mysteries that have remained mysteries down to our own time, in spite of all the work of intervening generations of men.

Albert, though so great a scientist in the strictest sense of the term, was made Provincial, the superior of a large district of the Order, by the Dominicans, and Bishop of Ratisbon by the Pope. Still other ecclesiastical dignities would surely have been his, only that he deliberately avoided them and preferred to do his writing and investigating in the peaceful solitude of the cloister. After his death he was proclaimed Blessed, and there is no question but that he will before long be raised to the altars of the Catholic Church as a Saint. There is no hint anywhere in his life that his scientific attainments and investigations hindered his advancement in his Order or in the Church, or caused him to be looked on in any way with suspicion.

Our other great scientist of the thirteenth century was Pope John XXI, the Ophthalmologist Pope. The sketch of his life illustrates, if possible more clearly even than that of Albert, that far from there being any friction between scientific scholars and investigators and theologians in the thirteenth century, the scientists were held in high honor, since one of them, Peter of Spain, who had taught medicine in several medical schools and had written a little book on eye diseases that has attracted much attention in recent years, because of the amount of knowledge of the subject that it displays, was, after having passed through the dignities of Archbishop and Cardinal, finally selected as Pope.

Probably the most surprising biography in the present series for those who have been accustomed to think that Church opposition prevented the development of science in the Middle Ages, is that of Guy De Chauliac, the father of modern surgery. We are so prone to think that surgery is a comparatively modern development and that there was no surgery to speak of until the nineteenth century, that it is a rather rude shock to find a great surgeon who was clergyman and a Chamberlain of the Popes about the middle of the fourteenth century. What Guy de Chauliac knew about surgery we learn, not from tradition nor from chance remarks of historians, nor from over-wrought panegyrics of his contemporaries, but from his wonderful text-book on surgery which for two centuries after his time was the most used text-book of the subject in practically all of the medical schools of Europe. In a word, we have first-hand evidence of the most valuable kind.

Anyone who still doubts about the cultivation of science or of the development of applications of science in the Middle Ages need only read the life of De Chauliac to be utterly disillusioned and to be given an entirely new idea with regard to science in the Middle Ages. There is scarcely a feature of our modern surgery that is not completely anticipated in Guy de Chauliac's work. He trephined the skull for injury and for abscess of the brain, and insisted that whenever there was a depressed fracture the bone had to be lifted or the patient would not recover. He opened the thorax in order to evacuate pus, and indicates exactly where openings should be made in order to secure proper emptying of the pathological fluids. He insists that whenever the intestines are wounded, the perforations in them

must be closed or the patient will die. He gives
very exactly the technique of sewing up wounds
of the intestines, and even invented a special
needleholder for that purpose. He operated
very commonly for hernia, but declared that
many patients were operated on for this affection
more for the benefit of the surgeon's pocket than
for their own good. What he teaches with regard to taxis for hernia remained the common
teaching of the medical schools for nearly five
centuries. With regard to fractures his detailed
instructions are not without value for most cases
even now, and they were the best of their kind
for several centuries. He describes the introduction of a catheter in difficult cases with the careful detail of a man who has evidently had large
experience in the matter. He even describes
many anatomical anomalies and shows how they
may prove serious obstacles to the surgeon.

After reading De Chauliac's *Grande Chirurgie*.
which may be obtained in many editions, no one
can thereafter maintain for a moment that applications of science were neglected in the
Middle Ages and above all that surgery did not
develop down to our time. It has been said over
and over again that the reason why surgical progress was in abeyance during the Middle Ages
was that the Church had forbidden clergymen
to practise it; and, as the only scholars of that
time belonged to the clerical order, therefore
surgery was left to the ignorant barber surgeons
and did not reach that development or receive

that attention which would otherwise have been the case. Such declarations are founded entirely on an ignorance as complete as it is presumptuous of the real history of surgery. These statements are made by historians who know nothing about the history of surgery during the thirteenth and fourteenth centuries and who therefore conclude that there must have been no surgery. As in the minds of these writers the Church is to be held responsible for all the blameworthy things that happened during this period, therefore she must be held accountable also for this failure of surgery. Now we know that the most wonderful period in the history of surgery, except the latter half of the nineteenth century, came during the thirteenth and fourteenth centuries, and that the great surgeons were all clergymen, and that the greatest of them all, Guy de Chauliac, who well deserves the name of father of modern surgery, was the Chamberlain and intimate friend of three of the Avignon Popes. Let us hope that the Church will be accorded her due meed of praise for this as she has been unduly blamed for what we now know to have been a completely mistaken notion of the real history of surgery.

In the fifteenth century astronomy took a new flight and developed into a science that was to dominate men's minds during the sixteenth and seventeenth centuries. The greatest contributor to this new state of affairs was of course Copernicus. His greatest predecessor, however, was

Johann Müller who under the name of Regiomontanus came to be acknowledged as one of the
greatest of pioneers in modern astronomical
knowledge. It was Regiomontanus's calendars
that were used by the Spanish and Portuguese
navigators in making their great voyages of discovery. Almost beyond doubt Columbus had a
copy of these when he made his famous prophecy
of the occurrence of an eclipse of the moon
which so impressed the American Indians when
they began to be impatient of the exactions of
some of the members of the expedition and
threatened to bring them no more supplies, and
to cause other difficulties for them. Regiomontanus's career as a scientist was capped by his
being invited to Rome in order to correct the
Calendar, and by his elevation to the dignity of
Bishop of Ratisbon, a successor after two
hundred years of Albertus Magnus in that See,
because the Pope was so impressed with his
piety and learning.

The last four centuries of history, so far as
the relations of the Catholic clergymen to science are concerned, are well summed up in the
articles on "The Jesuits in Astronomy" and
"Clergymen as Pioneers in Electricity." By
those outside the Church and unfamiliar with her
true history it would ordinarily be assumed that,
since in the case of Galileo the Popes had been
presumably so pronounced in their opposition to
astronomy, the great Order placed directly
under the control of the Popes and priding itself

on carrying out the wishes of the Papacy to the letter, would not be found cultivating this forbidden science. Quite the contrary is the truth. They were the most ardent students of it for the half century before and the century and a half after the trial of Galileo, that is, all during the life of the Order before its suppression. Some of the greatest of the astronomers of these two centuries are numbered amongst the Jesuits. The new Society, refounded in the nineteenth century, has continued this tradition, and one of the greatest of nineteenth-century astronomers was Father Secchi, S.J.

The phenomena of electricity were so interesting that it might well have been said that if clergymen had any freedom to devote themselves to scientific subjects, they would surely have taken up the investigation of some of these wonderful manifestations during their leisure hours. Most people know so little about the history of electricity that they would be apt to say at once that the fact that there are no clerical names that they know, prominent in the history of electricity is a proof that there must have been some ecclesiastical regulation or other churchly motive to deter them from this study. This is only another case of not knowing the real history of the science and then making much of the ignorance to decry the Church's attitude to science. Just as soon as the details of the history of electricity are gathered it becomes clear that some of the best pioneer work in nearly every department of electrical science was done by Catholic clergymen in the learned leisure afforded them from clerical duties. It is really surprising how many clerical names are associated with important discoveries, inventions, and suggestive conclusions in electricity. This chapter, like that on " The Jesuits in Astronomy," shows Catholic clergymen down to our own time constantly, consistently, and profoundly, and successfully interested in science.

The best proof of the serious, widespread interest of Catholic churchmen in science is to be found in the statistics of their place in science that may be gleaned from such a book as Poggendorf's *Biographical Dictionary of the Exact Sciences.* In this work, which is accepted as authoritative by the world of science, there are in the first two volumes the names of 8,847 contributors to science from the beginning of human history until 1863. This list embraces some twenty-five centuries. No inconsiderable proportion of these were before the introduction of Christianity. In spite of this a little more than ten per cent of all the names in this work are those of Catholic clergymen. As a rule contributors to science who were distinguished enough to secure a place in this work belonged to professions which required them to occupy themselves with scientific subjects, and it would naturally be supposed that from among these would come all but a very small proportion of the distinguished scientific investigators and dis-

coverers. In spite of the presumed improbabil-
ity of those outside of scientific circles securing
a place, more than one in ten of all these distinguished scientists came from the ranks of the
Catholic clergy. This can only mean that a very
large number of the churchmen of all periods
occupied themselves with things scientific in the
leisure afforded them by their clerical vocation,
and that nearly a thousand of them reached
noteworthy distinction in their avocation.

In the sketch of the Jesuit astronomers I have
called particular attention to the fact that nearly
one-half of these distinguished clerical scientists
were Jesuits. The Jesuits have been in existence
for less than three centuries and a half. The
reason for this preponderance of Jesuits in the
list of scientists is that they were the teachers,
and it was not only an avocation but a vocation
for them to do good work in science. When he
applies himself deliberately to science the Catholic clergyman, because of his devotion to his
work, is likely to be successful to a remarkable
degree, and this the Jesuits were. If there had
been any question of any overt or latent opposition to science in the Church, then this great
feature of the modern history of science would
be lacking, for the Jesuits, influenced by this
Church spirit with which they were so closely in
touch, would have kept aloof from science. In a
word it is very clear that, far from there being
any opposition to science on the part of the
Church, there was not only complete liberty but

even ecclesiastical encouragement for devotion to science, as far as that was compatible with religious duties.

These two series of sketches of Catholic churchmen in science seem to me then to place beyond all doubt the fact that there was not the slightest opposition to science on the part of the Catholic Church as a matter of ecclesiastical policy, though there may have been incidents in which ecclesiastics occasionally were found opposed to certain scientists. Nothing is commoner in the history of science than to find that even distinguished scientific bodies at times ignored or even bitterly opposed scientists who were doing great original work. The spirit of conservatism in men often leads them to oppose new truths because they are unfamiliar. If churchmen should occasionally have done this same thing, it is only what might be expected. Such incidents are much less common in Church history than is usually thought, however, and as a matter of fact most people know but one, the Galileo case, and utterly misunderstand and misrepresent the significance of that. The Galileo affair was entirely a personal matter and not at all a question of Church policy.

In other books I have treated other phases of this question of the supposed opposition of the Church to science. The great discoverers in science, above all for instance in recent medical science,[1] usually considered most unorthodox in

[1] See *Makers of Modern Medicine*, Fordham University Press, 1906.

its tendencies, were faithful sons of the Church. The same thing is true for electricity, for astronomy, and for old-time medicine, and books on these are in preparation. In *The Popes and Science* [2] I have shown that the Popes were as generous patrons of the medical schools of the last seven centuries (and all the sciences were cultivated in the medical schools until our day) as they were of art and of literature. The whole question of opposition between Church and Science rests on no better basis than ignorance of the real details of the history of science, and on the manifest purpose of certain writers and historians outside the Church to make it clear that the Popes and Catholic ecclesiastics exercised a deterrent influence on men's minds in this regard, lest science should disturb faith. It has come to be universally conceded now, however, that there is no essential opposition between science and faith; that the greatest scientists in all ages have been the most faithful believers, and that devout churchmen have in every age been great pioneers in science.

[2] Fordham University Press, 1908.

II.

ALBERTUS MAGNUS, PHILOSOPHER, THEOLOGIAN, SCIENTIST.

WE must be on our guard against giving interpretations (of Scripture) which are hazardous or opposed to science and so exposing the word of God to the ridicule of unbelievers. —AUGUSTINE, *De Genesi.*

IN studying nature we have not to inquire how God the Creator may as He freely wills, use His creatures to work miracles and thereby show forth His power : we have rather to inquire what nature with its immanent causes can naturally bring to pass.— ALBERT, *De Coelo et Mundo.*

THE aim of natural science is not simply to accept the statements of others, but to investigate the causes that are at work in nature.—ALBERT, *De Mineralibus.*

Magnus es, at major fieri dum ALBERTE, recusas
Dispeream, si quid majus hic orbis habet.

ALBERTUS MAGNUS, O. P.

II.

ALBERTUS MAGNUS,
PHILOSOPHER, THEOLOGIAN, SCIENTIST.

THERE are very few men, probably not more than can be counted easily on the fingers of the two hands, with whose names in history are associated the epithet " Great." As a rule, those who have it as even a more or less constant attribute are supposed to have merited it because of prowess in war. It probably will be a surprise to most people to have it called to their attention that there is one scholar in history to whom by universal consent the epithet has been so constantly attributed that most readers when they meet the word do not think of it as an adjective, but consider it to be a portion of his proper name. Albert von Bollstadt has *Magnus* or Great so intimately associated with his name that, as in the case of Charlemagne, it has become quite identified with him and probably most readers of history never think of either of them except with the epithet in mind. When we find that Albert was born in the heart of the Middle Ages, at the end of the twelfth or the beginning of the thirteenth century, the surprise is likely to be emphasized that at this portion of human history should have come the one scholar whose name is forever " the Great."

Even more interesting than the fact that Albert should have been proclaimed " the Great " for scholarship in the Middle Ages is the circumstance that, because of the breadth of his genius and interests, he probably deserves the title more than any other scholar who has ever lived. He more nearly reached universality of knowledge in his time than perhaps it has ever been given to any man alive. I say this deliberately, knowing how much Aristotle succeeded in exhausting human knowledge in his time, but appreciating the fact that Albert's contemporaries who knew their Aristotle very well called him a new Aristotle, appreciating that he had in addition depths of knowledge in many developments of Christian revelation as well as in the evolution of modern scientific ideas, that were far in advance of the old Greek philosopher. Of course it may be thought that at this time, in the thirteenth century, it would not be much for a man to exhaust human knowledge, because men did not know very much. Those who think that, however, know nothing of the curricula of the Universities of the thirteenth century, and especially ignore the fact that men's minds were just as inquisitive and succeeded in finding quite as satisfactory answers to the more important questions that concern man and his destiny as any that are accepted at the present time.

It is indeed amusing to note how confidently

men who know nothing at all about the Middle
Ages—and are indeed quite willing to confess that they know nothing—assume that there
cannot have been any education or any interest
in science in those times worth while talking
about. For, just as soon as men investigate for
themselves the subject of education and scientific knowledge at that period, their ideas change
and they begin not only to respect but to admire
the great work done by thinkers and educators
in those misunderstood ages. Literally men come
to scoff and remain to pray. The more one
knows about the Middle Ages the less does one
say in depreciation of them. Just as soon as
one studies faithfully any special feature of the
work they did, at once lack of comprehension
changes to respect and then to reverence for
their industrious, misjudged and calumniated
scholars.

This is as true for men of science as for those
who are interested in art and literature. A
typical example is Prof. Huxley. Surely if
there was anyone who might be expected to consider what had been done in the Middle Ages
as unworthy the attention of a modern scientific
educator it would be the great Darwinian con-
troversialist. He had studied the educational
situation in the Universities of the Middle Ages,
however, for himself, and had not assumed
that he possessed a knowledge of them *a priori*.
Accordingly in his inaugural address as Rector
of the University of Aberdeen, some thirty

years ago,[1] he said: "The scholars seem to have studied Grammar, Logic, and Rhetoric; Arithmetic and Geometry; Astronomy; Theology; and Music. Thus, their work, however imperfect and faulty, judged by modern lights, it may have been, brought them face to face with all the leading aspects of the many-sided mind of man. For these studies did really contain, at any rate, in embryo—sometimes it may be in caricature—what we now call Philosophy, Mathematical and Physical Science and Art. *And I doubt if the curriculum of any modern University shows so clear and generous a comprehension of what is meant by culture, as this old Trivium and Quadrivium does.*"[2]

Huxley has no illusions with regard to the backwardness of the Middle Ages in education or in science. He has not assumed to know all about the period of which he really knows nothing and then talks as if he knew all about it. He had gone into the investigation of the details of the subject before making his declarations and as a consequence he differs completely from those who have only a pretence of knowledge in the matter. His opinion thus frankly expressed always recalls to me the expression of a famous American humorist, Josh Billings, which I like to repeat because it sums up so thoroughly the significance of many opin-

[1] *Science and Education Essays*, Thomas H. Huxley. New York: Appleton & Co., 1896.

[2] Italics ours.

ions held by educators who ought to know better with regard to the history of education. Josh Billings, writing as Uncle Esek in the *Century* twenty-five years ago, said: "It is not so much the ignorance of mankind that makes them ridiculous as the knowing so many things that ain't so."

As a matter of fact, as I think I have shown in my book *The Thirteenth—Greatest of Centuries,*[3] there probably never was a hundred years in human history that produced such great men, gave rise to so many important movements, accomplished so much that was to have enduring influence in art, in literature, in education, and in democracy, as this century with which Albert's long life is so nearly coincident. The surprise with regard to the epithet Great is rather increased than diminished by this consideration, however, because he received this name which has clung so tenaciously to him from these generations of the thirteenth century, themselves so fruitful in supremely accomplished scholars, men with wonderful power to express in every department of human endeavor the thoughts that were in them. If they called him Great, then it is no wonder that succeeding centuries have adopted this title, until now it has become a part of Albert's name and constitutes the ready way by which we differentiate him most easily from many other Alberts in history.

[3] Catholic Summer School Press, N. Y., 1907.

Perhaps the most interesting phase of the history of Albert's right to the title, so far as the modern world is concerned, would be the fact that it was largely due to his knowledge of science.

The assumption that there was no study of nature in the early times of the Universities is one of those curious unfounded traditions which exist in people's minds and which the critical student of history finds it hard to account for. Anyone who wants to realize how much nature study there was in the thirteenth century should read his Dante with attention. In a chapter on the University Man and Science in my book *The Popes and Science,*[4] I call attention to a few of the details of Dante's knowledge of natural science and his interest in everything in nature. There is scarcely a poet in the modern time, no matter how recent or how much he has been trained in modern scientific nature study, who exhibits as much familiarity as Dante with all the round of sciences as they were known in his time. He does not parade his erudition. He uses his knowledge merely incidentally in order to bring out his meaning more clearly by figures drawn from science. There is no doubt that what we have from his pen in this matter represents only a little of what he actually knew, yet even that little shows a man familiar with phases

[4] *The Popes and Science,* Fordham University Press, N. Y. City.

of science utterly foreign to most of our modern poets.

It will not be too much, then, to say that Albertus Magnus received his title of Great to a considerable degree because of his knowledge of the physical sciences and the wonderful evolution in what we now call science that his suggestive original work effected. Science was a very inchoate department of knowledge at the beginning of the thirteenth century. Three-quarters of a century later, when Albert came to die, the deep and firm foundations of modern physical science had been laid, and at least one other great scientific investigator, who had probably been for a time a student with Albert, had done work in the physical sciences that was to make his name famous as one of the great scientists of all time and deserve for him the title unfortunately usurped by a namesake, who came three centuries later, of the founder of the experimental method. Roger Bacon and Albert accomplished the great initial work which means so much for science; they stepped across the boundaries of the unknown and blazed paths along which it was comparatively easy for subsequent generations to follow them in the mazes of scientific discovery. This is the aspect of Albert's life which is likely to appeal to a generation interested mainly in physical science.

Quite apart from this controversial standpoint, however, the most interesting feature of Albert the Great's life is his profound interest in physical science. We have come to limit the meaning of the word science to those branches of knowledge which are concerned with natural objects and which may be developed by the observation and the study of nature. Ordinarily we assume that nature study is a modern habit of mind. We are indeed inclined to criticize the founders of the Universities and the faculties of them for several centuries for not having devoted more time to the study of nature around them. They are supposed to have occupied themselves only with books and with book-learning. One reason for this is usually declared to have been that the Church, which was a very prominent factor in the Universities, feared the development of science lest it should disturb men's minds and take them away from their simple faith in religious truth. The very attitude of mind of the scientist, that of an inquirer, is supposed to be entirely opposed to that calm acceptance of dogmas on authority which the Church considered the ideal attitude of the human mind all during the Middle Ages.

It is quite unnecessary to say that it is impossible to give anything like a full account of Albert's life in the brief space at our command here. Besides his scientific career there is another phase of his life that deserves to be called especially to attention. This is the fact that while his own generation called him Great and subsequent generations adopted their opinion, the Church of which he was so devout a member all during life, always looked up to him as an ideal churchman, and nearly five centuries after his death raised him to her altars and gave him the title of Blessed. There is no doubt that before many years have passed this will be replaced by the title of Saint, which he will share with his great pupil and fellow-worker, St. Thomas Aquinas. Already the cause of his canonization has been, at the suggestion of the Bishops of Germany, formally begun. The title will add nothing to his glory or merit, but will proclaim him one of those men whom the Christian Church considers to have lived their lives more for others than for themselves, for that is, I suppose, the simplest definition of a saint. When we reflect, then, that this ideal churchman was a great scientist, and that indeed most of his intellectual merit consists of his discoveries in science, it makes a curious contradiction of the old tradition of Church opposition to science during the Middle Ages.

Albert's life contradicts many other false impressions held with regard to the Middle Ages besides its supposed neglect of science, and makes it very clear that about the same condition of affairs obtained with regard to education in the thirteenth century as in our own time. It is sometimes said that the nobility paid very little attention to education at this time. Some of them are even declared to have been proud of the fact that they did not know indeed how to read and write. It is evident that this

meant no more than the declarations of successful business men in the modern time who, not
having had the advantage of university education themselves, sometimes assert that such an
education is a detriment rather than a benefit.
The two greatest scholars of the thirteenth century, Albert and Aquinas, were both descended
from noble families, and not noble families of
the lower order, but, on the contrary, of very
high rank.   While Aquinas was a younger son
of the Count of Aquino, and what we know of
his elder brothers would seem to indicate that
they cared very little for the things of the mind,
it would be entirely wrong to conclude from this
example that such intellectual interests were rel-
egated to younger sons, for Albert was the eld-
est son of the Count of Bollstadt.

Albert was born at Lauingen in Suabia about
the end of the twelfth or the beginning of the
thirteenth century.   There is a considerable difference of opinion as to the exact date.   Some
historians place it as early as 1193; others set it
down as late as 1205 or 1206.   The evidence for
the later date is more convincing.   It is enough
for us to know that Albert's life, like that of
Cardinal Newman in the nineteenth century, ran
almost coincident with his century.   We know
practically nothing of his early years or of the
education which he received.   It is very probable
that whatever preparatory education he received
was obtained from tutors under the parental
roof.   When scarcely more than a boy, certainly

not more than sixteen or seventeen years of age, he was sent to pursue his studies at the University of Padua. At this time there were two famous Universities in Italy, one at Bologna, the specialty of which was the study of law, and the other at Padua, distinguished for the opportunities afforded for education in the liberal arts. There is a tradition that Albert had a special predilection for these and a taste for languages which was to serve him in good stead later in life.

The exact date of Albert's entrance to the University of Padua is unknown and the length of his stay there is uncertain. The first definite evidence that we have with regard to him as a young man is his entrance into the Order of St. Dominic. He was attracted to the Order by being brought in contact with Blessed Jordan of Saxony, the second Master-General of the Order. The date of his entrance is definitely known to have been about 1222. Whether he continued his studies in Italy after he became a Dominican is not known. When next we hear of him he has completed his studies and is teaching theology in various places in what we now know as South Germany. There are records of his having occupied the chair of Professor of Theology at Hildesheim, at Freiburg in Breisgau, at Ratisbon, at Strasburg, and at Cologne. It was while he was teaching at Cologne, basing his lectures on the well-known *Book of Sentences* of Peter Lombard, that in 1245 he was selected to represent the Dominican Order in the great University of Paris.

There had been considerable jealousy of the religious orders at Paris. The Franciscans and Dominicans shortly after their foundations both established houses in the French capital, in order that their young men might have the advantage of the University life. Very probably also, besides the opportunity to hear various professors which was there afforded so abundantly, the orders wished their young men to have the advantage of the libraries and of various educational opportunities provided in Paris at this time. Both the Franciscans and Dominicans had tried to secure certain special privileges for the members of their orders. They wished to have the University recognize at full value certain courses taken in the religious houses of the orders and for this asked to have their professors given University rights. For a time the University authorities refused any such special privileges. The Pope, as the ultimate authority in all University matters throughout the world, had to be appealed to, and it was only after considerable delay and after the subject had been much discussed and the whole question of the rights of religious orders established by many of their learned men, that special privileges were accorded to the orders. We owe St. Thomas Aquinas's great work on the religious orders to this controversy. In the meantime both the Franciscans and Dominicans made it a point to send some of their most distinguished teachers and pupils to Paris in order that they might be well represented and that the prestige of their work might obtain the privileges demanded.

Albert had been teaching at Cologne in the year 1245 when he received the direction to go to Paris. With him at Cologne at the time was Thomas Aquinas, whose genius only his great teacher as yet really suspected. Thomas accompanied his master to Paris and they seem to have studied there together. Albert received the degree of doctor in the University of Paris, and in 1248 returned, Thomas once more with him, to Cologne, where the University had been reorganized. Albert now became the Rector of the University of Cologne, and the prestige of his success at Paris and the fact that he brought back with him the traditions of that great University did much to make this *studium generale,* as Universities were then called, a popular place, for German students at least. Thomas became the second professor and the *magister studentium*—master of students—a term about equivalent to that of Dean at the present time. His duties were to care for the students in all that related to the direction of their studies, though doubtless whatever of discipline was required also fell into his hands.

It was during the next six years, while Albert was the Rector of the University of Cologne, that he somehow found the time to write his great works on Physical Science. These are on

nearly every subject connected with what we
now call science. He has a treatise on Physics,
on Meteors, on Minerals, on The Heavens and
The Earth, on The Nature of Places, and on The
Passions of the Air, the curious symbolic expression which he used for storms or atmos-
pheric disturbances or what we would now call
meteorology. In the biological sciences he has
treatises on Plants, on Animals, on Animal
Locomotion and Nutrition and Nutritives, on
Generation and Corruption, on Age, on Death
and Life, and on Respiration. In psychology he
has treatises on The Soul, on Sense and Sensa-
tion, on Memory, on Sleep and Waking, on
the Intellect, and on the Nature and Origin of
the Soul. When we consider that there are all
sorts of treatises on philosophic and metaphysical subjects besides these, is it any wonder that
his contemporaries called him the universal
doctor or that Engelbert, a writer of the time,
calls him the wonder and the miracle of his age?

Of course the ordinary impression of people
of the modern time who read these titles will be
that this medieval schoolman could have known
very little about these subjects and that what
he wrote must be mainly a tissue of absurdities.
Absurd things there are in Albert's writings,
but almost without exception he states these on
the authority of someone else and nearly always
adds his own disbelief in them. Scholars who
have studied Albert's works most faithfully
have thought the most of them. Among these

must be included not only those whose sympathies, because of religious motives, would naturally go out to Albert, but those who would on that same ground judge him most severely. We have the testimony of some very distinguished modern scientists to the depth and breadth of Albert's knowledge, while the testimonies which make little of him come from men who confess that they did not take the trouble to read him and who gather their opinions from others equally negligent or lacking the industry for this task.

Indeed for most of what we have just said with regard to Albert's wide knowledge in the sciences we can have ample confirmation without looking farther afield than to so well-known an authority as Humboldt, the distinguished German physical scientist of the first half of the nineteenth century, who in his *Kosmos* has this to say of Albert:

Albertus Magnus was equally active and influential in promoting the study of natural science and of the Aristotelian philosophy. His works contain some exceedingly acute remarks on the organic structure and physiology of plants. One of his works bearing the title of *Liber Cosmographicus de Natura Locorum* is a species of physical geography. I have found in it considerations of the dependence of temperature concurrently on latitude and elevation, and on the effect of different angles of incidence of the sun's rays in heating the ground, which have excited my surprise.

In the chapter of my book, *The Thirteenth— Greatest of Centuries,* on " What They Studied at the Universities," I have discussed some additional evidence that we have with regard to each of these sciences for which Humboldt gives words of praise to his medieval predecessor in the knowledge of most of what was known in their respective days. Here I may only call attention to the fact that Humboldt evidently considers that Albert had made distinct contributions to botany and especially to the physiology of this science, to physical geography, to meteorology, and to astronomy. For some of these subjects we have further evidence that is of very great interest. M. Meyer, in his *History of Botany*, says that "No botanist who lived before Albert can be compared to him, unless Theophrastus, with whom he was not acquainted; and after him none has painted nature in such living colors or studied it so profoundly until the time of Conrad Gessner and Cesalpino." We may say that, according to his biographer, Sighart:

He was acquainted with the sleep of plants, with the periodical opening and closing of blossoms, with the diminution of sap through evaporation from the cuticle of the leaves, and with the influence of the distribution of the bundles of vessels on the folial indentations. His minute observations on the forms and variety of plants intimate an exquisite sense of floral beauty. He distinguished the star from the bell-floral, tells us that a red rose will turn white when submitted to the vapor of sulphur, and makes some very sagacious observations on the subject of germination.

Indeed, Albert's contributions to botany seem

so valuable to Meyer, the modern German historian of that subject, that he republished the great schoolman's treatise in six books on Vegetables and Plants. This republication did more than anything else to disabuse modern scholars of the idea that the writings on natural science of the Middle Ages were either ridiculous or trivial in importance. Since this republication some thirty years ago, Albert's other contributions to science have become much better known, and with him to know is always to admire. As a consequence, frequent tributes have been paid to the universal doctor, and men have come to realize how wise the generation was in which he lived. Pagel, the German historian of medicine, whom we have already quoted with regard to Albert, does not hesitate to say that his style, far from being uninteresting, is full of information, and that when he accepts curious stories on the authority of others, he does not fail to mention that fact and usually gives some hint that he did not credit the story himself. In a word, his was no merely encyclopedic knowledge, but it had been garnered in a proper critical spirit.

With regard to other phases of Albert's scientific work, we have the same good modern authority as to its thorough-going significance. Pagel, who has written the chapters on Medieval Medicine and Science in Puschmann's three-volume *History of Medicine,* says that the treatise on the nature of places which Humboldt

praises, contains many very interesting suggestions with regard to ethnography and physiology. Pagel also finds words of commendation
for various portions of Albert's work on Physics.
This discussed the principles of what used to
be called Natural Philosophy, and its eight
books, while forming a commentary on Aristotle's Physics, go far beyond the Greek Philosopher in their treatment of the underlying principles of physical nature.

With regard to chemistry, there are many interesting contributions from Albert's pen. He
was, as we shall see, the first to make it very
clear that the substances which were called
spirits in the olden times because they often ex-
ploded and did serious damage, were only manifestations of natural forces and not of occult or
other-worldly powers. One of Albert's treatises
on chemistry bears the name " The Causes and
the Properties of the Elements." His treatise
on minerals contains, according to Pagel, besides
an extended description of the ordinary pecu-
liarities of minerals, which shows his own acute-
ness and that of his generation in observing
even minute differences, a detailed description
of nearly one hundred different kinds of precious stones. This book contains also a mine of
information with regard to the metals, of which
Albert describes seven, and the other familiar
mineral substances of the time, salt, vitriol, alum,
arsenic, amber, niter, and marcasite.

Albert was particularly interested in all such

questions as relate to man and the higher animals. He gathered into a series of treatises all the knowledge of his own time and all that he could glean from the writings of those who had lived before him with regard to every phase of animal and human life. The result is that a list of his writings is a catalogue of works in science that can scarcely fail to astonish the modern mind, unaccustomed to the idea of interest in science, especially in the biological sciences, during the thirteenth century. Albert has two treatises on Generation and Corruption (*De Generatione et Corruptione*). He has a treatise on Respiration; another on The Motion of Animals (*De Animalium Locomotione*) which takes up the question both of the voluntary and involuntary motions performed by them. Then there is a treatise on The Senses (*De Sensibus*), another on Sleeping and Waking (*De Somno et Vigilantia*), and a third on Life and Death (*De Vita et Morte*). His studies in the psychology of animals and in human beings are especially interesting in the light of the fact that this subject has come to occupy so much attention in recent years. Besides his treatise on the Senses, Albert has a monograph on The Memory and The Imagination (*De Memoria et Imaginatione*); another, in two books, on the Intellect (*De Intellectu*); and a third, in three books, on The Soul (*De Anima*), in which, of course following the scholastic philosophy of the time, the soul is considered the vital principle of the body as well as the underlying principle of the intellect, and in which of course a vitalism that would be more popular just at the present time than at any other period for the last half century, is emphatically taught. Along this same line, Albert has a treatise on Youth and Old Age (*De Juventute et Senectute*), in which he discusses many of the important problems of human life and its relation above all to the development of the will and the character. There is scarcely a phase of the modern biological sciences, even that of the higher psychology, which is not touched upon by Albert, and in many passages he presents what are really marvelous anticipations of some supposedly very modern thought.

But Albert's devotion to the biological sciences did not keep him from paying serious attention to what we now call, in contradistinction to them, the physical sciences, the classified knowledge of inanimate things. Some of his work in physics and chemistry deserves to be better known because it constitutes special chapters in the history of these sciences.

One of the most interesting things that Albert did in these subjects was his investigation of the origin of gases. It had often been noticed that when men descended into certain caves or into mines, or into old wells, they lost their lives. This was usualy attributed to the devils who were supposed to inhabit such dark places, and who resented the coming-in of men. Sometimes when lights were carried into such places, instead of being merely extinguished, they proved to be the origin of serious explosions. This was, of course, attributed to the powers of darkness, who doubly resented the presence of light in their domain. Albert, however, did not accept any such explanation. He suggested that there were certain substances which emanated from the rocks or from the soil in these places which led to the deaths of men or of animals who wandered into them, or which caused the explosions when naked lights were carried into them. It was in his time, and it is usually considered to be the result of his initiative that the word *spirit* came to be applied very generally to such volatile substances as readily produced gas when heated and which thus give rise to explosions. The word *spiritus* had originally been employed for these substances, because they were supposed to contain within them certain evil spirits which resented the application of heat; but this idea was completely overturned by Albert's investigations.

In the light of all that we know about Albert's devotion to the physical sciences the attitude of many historians and scholars toward the question of the Church's relation to science at this time is amusing and somewhat amazing. President White, for instance, acknowledges Albert's wonderful contributions to science in every form, but attributes the fact that he should have paid so much attention to Philosophy and Theology to the opposition which he encountered as regards his scientific studies and publications.

Surely any such view as this utterly ignores the extraordinary vogue of Albert's books on sciences. They existed in many manuscript copies and were constantly reproduced by the slow labor of writing by hand. This must have required the unfailing devotion of his disciples and his Dominican brethren. His works were carefully preserved, written again and again, although they contain several million words, by successive generations of Dominicans, and they were looked upon not as suspicious books but as precious contributions to human knowledge. There is no account anywhere in Albert's life of any opposition aroused by his devotion to science.

So far indeed from the fact is President White's declaration with regard to Albert's deliberate neglect of physical science, in order that he might devote himself more to philosophy and theology, that Albert's books and writings on physical science loomed so large in the minds of his contemporaries and of the immediately succeeding generations, that one of the objections sometimes urged against Albert is that his interest in scientific subjects did not permit him to pay as much attention as he ought to the sacred sciences. This opinion was expressed rather emphatically by Henry of Ghent in his Ecclesiastical Writers (*De Scriptoribus Ecclesiasticis,* II, x). The list of Albert's published works on Philosophy, Theology, and Scripture forms, as is well remarked by his biographer in

The Catholic Encyclopedia, an all-sufficient vin-
dication from the charge that he neglected Theology and Sacred Sciences. With this side of
Albert's activity as a writer we have nothing to
do here, because we are interested only in his
scientific work.

Those who think that science as we know the
term at the present day is a modern invention
or a modern development of human intellectual
accomplishment, need only to read Albert's original works, and if they will take the trouble there
will be no doubt of the existence of not only the
most enthusiastic interest in natural science during the thirteenth century, but also the most successful elucidation of many of its problems.
The great foundations of most of the modern
sciences were then laid. We are prone to think
that at most a few paths were broken in the unknown land of natural science and that at best
the advances were few, the horizons distant, the
views shadowy. We are apt to imagine that only
a science or two, a little physics and chemistry
were touched upon, and that these were followed
with such curious mistaken notions as to make
any real advance impossible. We have been accustomed to make fun of the search for the philosopher's stone by which base metals would be
transmuted into the precious metals, but ten
years ago, apparently, we found the long-sought-
for philosopher's stone in the metal radium, for
by means of its emanations we can apparently
transform metals into one another. Radium

itself changes into helium, though both were thought to be elementary substances. And at the last meeting of the British Association for the Advancement of Science Sir William Ramsey announced the transmutation of copper and lithium by means of radium emanations. Our greatest of living chemists in the English-speaking world may not have solved the problem of metallic transmutation, as he thinks he has; but he frankly places himself beside the old alchemists in his work. Already a modern professor of chemistry had suggested that he would like to examine a mass of lead-ore carefully, and having extracted all the silver that occurs in lead-ore, would like to lay it aside for twenty years and see whether, at the end of that time he would not find more silver in the mass. His idea is evidently that lead in nature probably constantly changes into silver by slow degrees, so that the old alchemists were not so foolish, but, on the contrary, anticipated what is most modern in chemistry.

As a matter of fact, what strikes one after a while when he has become familiar with what was accomplished in science in the Middle Ages is that they should have anticipated so much of what is considered to be modern in science, and that, considering how far they went, it is amazing that in nearly seven centuries we have gone so little farther than they did. This is true, however, not only in chemistry and in physics, but in practically every department of natural science, for all of these were opened up and, as we have seen, Albert himself was a pioneer and great thinker in nearly every one of them, as good authorities in modern science familiar with his writings have declared.

Albert's attitude toward what we have come to recognize as the true method of science, the experimental method, is the best possible evidence for his great accomplishments in science. There are many who still believe that it was Francis Bacon at the beginning of the seventeenth century who laid the foundation of the inductive sciences. Any such opinion is founded entirely on ignorance of what was accomplished during the medieval centuries, and it has its only reason for being in that curious blindness which has led so many people during the last three or four centuries to be unable to see anything good in the Nazareth of the times before the so-called Reformation. All the real historians of science in the last twenty-five years have been rejecting the notion of the leadership of Francis Bacon in this matter and have been engaged in pointing out that he was only a publicist who had the good fortune to write a book on the subject that became popular, but that the real father of the inductive sciences was his great namesake Roger Bacon, nearly four centuries before. While this title of the great Franciscan of the thirteenth century is indisputable, there is no doubt that his sometime teacher Albert had anticipated most of the principles of experimental science and method even before Roger Bacon.

In the epigraphs at the beginning of this
sketch I have quoted some sentences from
Albert's writings that make it very clear how
much of dependence he placed on experiment in
science and how thoroughly he realized that this
was the only possible method of obtaining exact
knowledge with regard to natural objects.   In
bringing those epigraphs together it seemed
worth while to place beside them a great expression from St. Augustine conveying the same
truth in different language, for from Augustine
to Albert there is 800 years and the work of
these two has dominated Christianity for 1500
years, so that their spirit represents the real policy of the scholars and the genuine attitude of
mind of the great theologians.   Unfortunately
it is the custom of writers of history only too
often to take the expressions of obscure writers,
or chance remarks of such men as Augustine and
Albert, apart from their context, as indicative of
the attitude of the Church and of ecclesiastics
during this period to science.   The unfairness of
this is easy to understand, but it has represented
one of the ways in which history has been, if not
deliberately falsified, at least made to lean
toward the opinions of the writer rather than
to express the true significance of events.

There is no doubt at all of Albert's devotion
to theological science or of the magnificent results that he achieved therein.   In spite of all
that his great disciple St. Thomas Aquinas accomplished in this department, Albert still con-

tinued and continues to be looked upon as one
of the living authorities on this subject. It was
this great theologian, however, who declared in
his book on Minerals, "that the aim of natural
science is not simply to accept the statements of
others, but to investigate the causes that are at
work in nature." The rule that he thus laid
down for the sciences relating to inanimate
things, he applied also to the biological sciences
when he wrote about plants. In his treatise On
Plants (*De Vegetalibus,* VI. tr. ii, i) he says, in
an expression that has often been quoted since,
"experiment is the only sure method in such investigations." The wording of the original
Latin is worth remembering because of the deep
significance of the expression: *Experimentum
solum certificat in talibus.*

When we have all this before us from this
great physical scientist and theologian we are not
so surprised as we might otherwise be by his
famous declaration: "In studying nature we
have not to inquire how God the Creator may,
as He freely wills, use His Creatures to work
miracles and thereby show forth His power: we
have rather to inquire what nature with its immanent causes can naturally bring to pass." It
is this sentence occurring in his treatise on the
Heavens and the Earth that makes it very clear
how little of opposition there was in Albert's
mind between his faith and his science. One is
not surprised to find after this declaration that,
although Albert's favorite author was St. Au-

gustine, he preferred Aristotle to St. Augustine in matters of science. At the same time he did not hesitate to point out many errors in Aristotle; in fact, in his famous *Summa* of theology he devotes a lengthy chapter to the errors of the Greek philosopher and Albert thus shows that he still maintained the opinion which he had expressed in his Book of Sentences: " Whoever believes that Aristotle is a god must also believe that he never erred, but if one believes that Aristotle is a man, then beyond all doubt he was liable to err just as we are."

It is no wonder that we find that Roger Bacon, a greater physical scientist than Albert, thought much of his great predecessor, and, although he was rather inclined to be critical of his contemporaries and forerunners in science, had only praise for Albert. He said of him: " Albert was most serious, had a broad outlook on the world of knowledge and an immense capacity for work. He could therefore collect much information in the vast scene of writings." Albert was much more conservative than Roger Bacon, had much more of sympathy for the failure of others to follow him in his scientific work, a failure which constitutes one of the sources of that trouble that great original scientists nearly always prepare for themselves, and as a consequence, as Turner in his *History of Philosophy* has so well pointed out, he " contributed far more than Bacon did to the advancement of science in the thirteenth century." Roger Bacon has insisted

on how much of information Albert obtained
from books, but he knew that Albert must have
done much personal investigation. His use of
books, as has already been illustrated by his attitude toward the great Greek philosopher,
Aristotle, of whom he thought so much, was eminently critical and much more like that which
has become common in our own time than is to
be noted in any of his contemporaries.

Perhaps the most interesting phase of Albert's
knowledge for the modern times is his refusal
to accept some of the beliefs which were very
commonly credited in his time and which our
generation usually sets down as having been accepted by even the deepest scholars of the Middle
Ages. For instance, though many of his contemporaries believed in the possibility of the
transmutation of metals Albert did not, but on
the contrary, rather emphatically disapproved
of the notion and considered that any such
change was absolutely impossible. He thought
that substances as we know them were essentially different, and proclaimed that " art alone
cannot produce a substantial form." With regard to magic and its supposed marvelous power,
so commonly believed in even by the wisest in
the earlier Middle Ages, and which Albert found
so completely accepted by many of his great
predecessors and teachers, the great Dominican
scholar was very emphatic in his rejection of
all belief in it. He said, " I do not approve what
Avicenna and Algazel have said with regard to

fascination (or magic) because I believe that
magic can do no harm, that magical arts have
no power for evil, and they do not accomplish
any of the things that are feared from them."

With regard to other curious beliefs of his
time Albert maintained the same sceptical attitude. Even a cursory reading of his works
shows that he refused to accept many of the
fairy tales of science and of popular tradition
which were so commonly received in his time.
It is only great original minds of supreme depth
and force that are thus able to get away from
the delusions common in their time; and every
age, despite its self-complacent reproach of previous ages for their credulousness, may well
consider itself as subject to them. We have
them in our time, and only the great scholars
rise superior to them, as did Albert in the thirteenth century. His biographer, Sighart, has
collected a series of the fables and pseudo-scien-
tific stories which were rejected by Albert. His
paragraph helps to give us a better idea of what
the great scholar thus accomplished than perhaps
could be obtained in any other way. He says:

He treats as fabulous the commonly received idea, in
which Bede has acquiesced, that the region of the
earth south of the equator was uninhabitable, and considers that from the equator to the South Pole, the
earth was not only habitable, but in all probability
actually inhabited except directly at the poles, where
he imagines the cold to be excessive. If there be any
animals there, he says, they must have very thick skins
to defend them from the rigor of the climate, *and they*

are probably of a white color. The intensity of cold is, however, tempered by the action of the sea. He describes the antipodes and the countries they comprise, and divides the climate of the earth into seven zones. He smiles with a scholar's freedom at the simplicity of those who suppose that persons living at the opposite region of the earth must fall off, an opinion that can only rise out of the grossest ignorance, " for when we speak of the lower hemisphere, this must be understood merely as relative to ourselves." It is as a geographer that Albert's superiority to the writers of his own time chiefly appears. Bearing in mind the astonishing ignorance which then prevailed on this subject, it is truly admirable to find him correctly tracing the chief mountain chains of Europe with the rivers which take their source in each; remarking on portions of coast which have in later times been submerged by the ocean, and islands which have been raised by volcanic action above the level of the sea; noticing the modification of climate caused by mountains, seas, and forests, and the division of the human race, whose differences he ascribes to the effect upon them of the countries they inhabit! In speaking of the British Isles he alludes to the commonly received idea that another distant Island called Tile or Thule existed far in the Western Ocean, uninhabitable by reason of its frightful climate, but which, he says, has perhaps not yet been visited by man.

Nothing will so seriously disturb the complacency of modern minds as to the wonderful advances that have been made in the last century in all branches of physical science as to read Albert's writings. Nothing can be more wholesomely chastening of present-day conceit than to get a proper appreciation of the extent of the knowledge of the schoolmen. Nowhere can one

get a better notion of the immense amount of
even scientific information possessed by those
whom so many educated(!) people now call in
derision the scholastics than from Albert's writings, consulted at first-hand and not in the gar-
bled extracts of modern unsympathetic commentators.

But to turn to Albert's career. For six years
after his return from Paris he remained as what
we would now call the Rector of the University
of Cologne. His success in this responsible position naturally suggested other and higher posts
for his administrative ability. Accordingly in
1254 he was elected the Provincial of the Order
in Germany. This took him away from immediate touch with teaching and investigation, but
gave him abundant opportunities for the encouragement of learning in every department in all
the houses of his Order in Germany. His influence was felt everywhere. Two years after his
election as Provincial he went to Rome, in order
to defend the Mendicant Orders against the attacks which had been made upon them, particularly by William of St. Amour. The condemnation of William's book, " On the Latest Dangers of the Time," was secured from Pope
Alexander IV on 5 October, 1256. It is rather
interesting to realize how thoroughly appreciated
Albert must have been. He had been chosen
to go to Paris as the representative of what was
best in the intellectuality of his Order. He was
delegated to go to Rome to defend it against the

attacks of those who did not appreciate all the spirituality there was in the religious orders of the time. Evidently Albert was looked upon as a representative of all that was best in his Order.

How much Albert was thought of in Rome, though he was now at least fifty years of age and a large part of his life-work in the natural sciences and in the application of the experimental method had already been accomplished, may be appreciated from the fact that during his stay in the Papal capital he was appointed to fill the office of Master of the Papal Palace. This office had been instituted in the time of St. Dominic and was generally considered to be one of the highest honors that could come to a man. It was honorary rather than administrative, and was usually conferred on men who were chosen as the recipients of a signal expression of the approbation of the ecclesiastical authorities. That his selection for this office was no idle compliment paid to the man or the prestige of his name as a great scholar may be realized from the fact that he was asked at the same time to preach in Rome on the Gospel of St. John and on the Canonical Epistles. Then as now, only those were chosen to be public preachers in Rome of whose thoroughgoing orthodoxy and absolute concordance with the spirit and tradition of the Church there was not the slightest doubt.

The cares of office, however, apparently hung heavy on Albert's shoulders and he was not one of those for whom honors and dignities would make up for the time that he had to devote to administrative details. He was anxious to get back to his studies and investigations, his teaching, and his writings. He resigned the office of Provincial in 1257. His departure from Rome had relieved him of the cares of the office of Master of the Papal Palace. At once he devoted himself not only to his own studies, but to making the studies of the members of his Order more effective. Within a few years we can find him a prominent factor in the reorganization of the Dominican studies, which had been discussed for some time and finally taken up for formal action at the general chapter of the Order held at Valenciennes in 1259. This chapter laid down rules for the direction of the studies of the younger Dominicans and suggested methods of teaching by which their education would be made more efficient. The system of graduation was also modified in such a way as to make it sure that the graduates from Dominican schools would be in every way the equals of the graduates from the Universities.

It might be thought that the ideas of these men of the thirteenth century with regard to the methods of teaching and requirements of graduation would be very vague and indefinite. The members of the committee responsible for the new order of things then determined on were Albert, St. Thomas Aquinas, and Peter of Tarenpasia, who afterwards reached the distinction of being made Pope under the name of Pope In-

nocent V. Though his name is not so familiar
to modern scholars as those of the other two
members of this perhaps the most distinguished
committee for the revision of studies that ever
held sessions, he was the author of a series of
works on philosophy, theology, and canon law,
and of commentaries on the Epistles of St. Paul
and the Book of Sentences of Peter Lombard,
which are well known to scholars. For these
contributions to the philosophic and theological
literature of an especially copious century he is
sometimes spoken of as *Famosissimus Doctor*—
the most famous doctor. It is very evident that
the question of the organization of studies was
taken very much to heart by the Dominicans,
since they selected three such men as these for
the work, and since three such men were willing
to take the time from their own occupations and
were ready to devote their learning and experience to the subject.

Albert had become so much appreciated at
Rome that in spite of his own anxiety to remain
a simple Dominican and devote himself to his
studies he could not succeed in escaping promo-
tion to the hierarchy. In the year 1260 he was
selected as the Bishop of Ratisbon. As soon
as he heard of the proposed elevation to the
episcopacy, Albert tried to secure the cancella-
tion of the appointment and appealed for this
purpose to the Master General of the Dominicans. The latter endeavored as far as was possible to prevent the appointment of Albert, but

the Roman authorities were confident that
Albert's genius and administrative ability would
serve the best purposes of the Church as a
bishop.   Albert bowed his head in submission
then, and accepted the post.   After two years
he had succeeded in reorganizing the affairs of
the bishopric, and then at his earnest request he
was allowed to resign and he once more took up
the duties of a professor in the University of
Cologne.   Here he seems to have spent the next
eight years in peace in the midst of his favorite
occupations of investigating, writing, and teaching.   He was too great a man, however, to be
allowed to continue his work so peacefully, and
in 1270 we find him aiding St. Thomas in com-
bating certain of the philosophical heretics of
the time.

The great distinction of his life was yet to
come.   In 1274 he was summoned by Pope Gregory X to attend the Council of Lyons, in the
deliberations of which he took a most important
part as the direct representative of the Pope.
His colleague in this office of honor and respon-
sibility was his old pupil and life-long friend, St.
Thomas Aquinas.   Albert received the news of
St. Thomas's death as he himself was on the way
to the Council.   It proved a very serious blow to
him.   He declared that the light of the Church
had been extinguished.   Something of the beau-
tifully sympathetic relationship that had existed
between the two men can be appreciated from
the fact that ever afterwards the master could

not restrain his tears whenever the name of St. Thomas was mentioned. Many lives of these two great men have been written, and yet this special chapter of their beautiful friendship remains to have such treatment as it deserves. They were the two greatest geniuses of their age, probably also two of the greatest geniuses that ever lived. In spite of their occupation with the same questions, involving not a few differences of opinion on minor points, there seems never to have been anything to disturb the wondrous harmony of their friendship.

Albert was now past seventy years of age and might be expected to begin to lose something of the vigor of his intellectuality. When h: was nearly seventy-five, however, there is a flash of all his old mental brilliancy because of a movement on the part of certain writers and thinkers of the time to bring about the condemnation of the writings of St. Thomas, on the plea that St. Thomas had made too much and held in. too high estimation the old Pagan philosopher, Aristotle. Albert's physical strength even seemed renewed at this and he journeyed to Paris in order to defend the memory of his pupil. For a year more he continued to be the great scholar of his time and the light of his period. Then, in 1278, his memory began to go and his strong mind gave way. For a time he seems to have been without the use of his intellectual faculty in the rapidly advancing senile decay that came over him. He had been a man

of immense labors and this must have been another trial, in as far as he was conscious of it,
but, until the end, he retained his placidity and
peaceful acceptance of the will of God. With
his passing who can doubt that there departed
from the scene of his earthly labors one of the
most wonderful geniuses that the world has ever
known and one of the most original thinkers in
the history of the race. The more we know of
him, the more we admire the critical judgment
of an age that attached to his name for all time
the epithet Great, and the more we learn to appreciate the wisdom of the immediately succeeding generations, who gave him the title of the
Universal Doctor.

III.

JOHN XXI,
PHILOSOPHER, PHYSICIAN, POPE.

F<small>INIS</small> scientiarum est commodis
   humanis inservire et efficaciter
operari ad sublevanda vitae humanae
incommoda.—F<small>RANCIS</small> B<small>ACON</small>, L<small>ORD</small>
V<small>ERULAM</small>.

POPE JOHN XXI.

III.

PROBABLY nothing is more commonly accepted, even among the educated who are outside of the Catholic Church, than the tradition that, while the Church was the ruling force of the educational world of Europe, she was if not directly opposed to natural science at least very jealous of its advance, and ecclesiastics were prone to the persuasion that devotion to natural science almost surely undermined faith. This is supposed to be especially true with regard to the experimental sciences during the centuries before Luther's revolt. We all know that philosophy and the deductive sciences were encouraged. The inductive sciences, however, are often said to have been placed, if not under the ban of ecclesiastical regulations, at least under the discouragement of the Church to such a degree, that it is no wonder that progress in them was not made and that it was not until quite recent times that the physical sciences developed. According to commonly accepted ideas, only in proportion as the hold of the Church on education and on the minds of men generally became relaxed in the renaissance period did science begin to make serious pro-

gress, while it is only since the development of
the spirit of free thought that science has taken
her supreme place as the mistress of intellect.

Doubtless there are many people who consider
that this is the proper way to sum up the history of science until our own times. Such a
view, however, contains more misstatements,
more perversions of thought, more ignorance
of the real state of the history of science during
the Middle Ages, than could possibly be con-
densed into any equally brief space. It supposes
that there was no study of the physical sciences
to speak of during the Middle Ages, which is
absolutely untrue. I need say no more than
that there were some twenty medical schools
founded in Europe before the Fall of Constantinople in 1452, which is usually considered the
end of the Middle Ages, to show that the medical sciences were cultivated very assiduously.
These had a large number of students in attend-
ance and some of them were larger than most
of our medical schools of the present day.
Three years of preparatory study in logic and
philosophy were required for these schools, and
then three and sometimes four years in the study
of medicine, to which an additional year had
to be added if the student intended to practise
surgery before license to practise would be given.
Every single one of the modern sciences developed during the thirteenth century. Noteworthy
contributions were made to physics, chemistry,
physical geography, botany, meteorology, astron-

omy and, above all, to the subject of geography during that great century of educational activity when the universities were cast into their modern form.

The ecclesiastical authorities absolutely ruled in these Universities. The chancellor of the University was usually the archdeacon of the cathedral of the town in which the University was located. Most of the professors were clerics. Most of the students in those days were protected from various military impositions and political claims that might be put upon them by the civil authorities by belonging to the clerical order. It was churchmen then who developed the sciences and laid the foundations of what we now call the physical sciences. Still more wonderful than this, however, is the fact that the most distinguished contributors to the physical sciences were as a rule members of the religious orders, many of whom reached high dignities in the Church and some of the most distinguished of them were canonized after death. In other words, the ordinary impression with regard to the attitude of the Church in the Middle Ages toward science is founded on a misconception of the history of science and education. There is no excuse at all for its existence except that Protestant tradition which, beginning at the time of the so-called Reformation, blackened all the preceding centuries so as to justify the apostasy from the Church, by making it very clear that tor centuries the Church had been keeping people in ignorance and that this was the only way that their allegiance could be secured. In English-speaking countries this method succeeded so well that, until comparatively recent times, it was practically impossible to convince people that anything good could come out of the Nazareth of the time before the religious revolt in the Northern countries at the beginning of the sixteenth century it was before this time that were laid the foundations of all that is most interesting and important in modern life.

As a matter of fact success in scientific investigations during the Middle Ages often constituted at least one of the reasons why men received ecclesiastical preferment. Few men have ever done more for science in the strictest sense of that term than Albertus Magnus, whose life immediately precedes this. Here we need only say that he wrote altogether more than fifteen treatises on subjects connected with the physical sciences. Far from this intense and diffusive scientific activity bringing him into displeasure with his contemporaries and especially with the ecclesiastical authorities, it seems rather to have enhanced his reputation and led to his rapid ecclesiastical preferment. After having been the Provincial of his Order, the Dominican moreover, he was selected as Bishop of Ratisbon, and was one of the most honored and respected ecclesiastics of his time.

Thomas Aquinas, who has come to be the most honored scholar in the last thousand years of the Church's history, is another striking example of exactly the same kind. Not a little of his work was concerned with the physical sciences—as might be expected, for he was a favorite pupil of Albertus Magnus. As was the case with Albert, far from this hurting his career in any way it served only to add to the estimation in which he was held as the greatest allround scholar and most conservative thinker of his time. He was selected to be the theologian of the Pope, the personal representative of the Roman Pontiff in the discussion at the Council of Lyons. He was chosen to be Archbishop of Naples, and the Bulls of his appointment were actually issued when he was saved from the dignity which would have been so serious a hindrance to his work as an investigator in philosophy and in science, by his own protest and those of his friends that he should be permitted to devote himself to the writing of the greatest *Summa* of human knowledge that was ever planned.

What was true in the thirteenth remained true in the fourteenth and fifteenth centuries. The father of modern surgery, of whom it has been said that he was one of the greatest contributors to medicine of all time, was Guy De Chauliac, a sketch of whose life immediately follows this who was a cleric, the chamberlain of three popes as well as the physician-in-ordinary to them. There surely could have been no opposition to science while Chauliac was the confiden-

tial adviser for some thirty years of the popes
of the fourteenth century. The same thing was
true in the next century. The founder of modern astronomy is Regiomontanus, who first established an astronomical observatory in the
modern time and published tables of astronomical observations. He was called down to Rome
by the pope in order to correct the calendar, unfortunately dying before he had completed his
work, but not before the pope, as a reward for
his success in science as well as his faithfulness
to his ecclesiastical duties, had made him the
Bishop of Ratisbon. Cardinal Nicholas of Cusa
is another man of the fifteenth century who had
won distinction by his originality in science and
especially in astronomical thought before he was
made Cardinal and sent to Germany to help in
the reform of abuses in that country.

With distinguished scientists as papal cham-
berlains, bishops, archbishops, and cardinals,
when one reads history aright, it is not near so
surprising as it might otherwise seem that there
should have been a distinguished scientist who
became pope. This was the famous Peter of
Spain, who had been a physician and a professor
in several universities before he was made bishop
and eventually chosen as pope. It is rather curiously interesting to note that in the picture of
Paradise where Dante [1] has enumerated some of
the distinguished scholars who have a place in
heaven, Bonaventure, Augustine, Chrysostom,

[1] *Paradiso*, Canto XII, 135.

Anselm, and Abbot Joachim, with Hugh of St.
Victor, he also notes the presence of him

. . . of Spain,
Who through twelve volumes full of light descants.

The reference is to Peter of Spain, and Plumptre
notes that this is the only pope whom Dante
speaks of as in Paradise, though he has mentioned a number of occupants of the papacy as
dwelling in other portions of the after-world.

This was Pope John XXI, as he is usually
denominated in history, though owing to the difficulty of deciding with regard to certain dubious
popes in time of schism, he has also been called
Pope John XIX and Pope John XX. There has
even been some confusion between him and one
of his successors, the Avignon Pope John XXII,
and certain cyclopedias have attributed works
that were surely written by Pope John XXI to
this French Pope of the next century. In *Janus,*
which is the International Archives for the History of Medicine and for Medical Geography,
some ten years ago,[2] Dr. J. B. Petella reviewed
all that is to be found in literature with regard
to Pope John XXI, and makes it very clear that
he was a physician before he became pope, that
he wrote a little book on the affections of the
eyes which is not only a medical but also a literary classic, because it is one of the earliest Ital-

[2] *Janus Archives Internationales pour l'Histoire de la
Médicine et pour la Géographie Médicale.* Deuxième
Année. Amsterdam, 1897-1898.

ian writings that we possess, and has been used for dictionary purposes by the Academia della Crusca. Moreover this Pope during his occupation of the Holy See probably directed the writing of a little book called the *Treasure of the Poor* for the popularization of medicine for those who could not afford a physician's services.

John XXI was not however the first pope in history noted for attainments in science. At least two popes in centuries not long before his reached distinction in the scientific circles of their time. The first of these was Gerbert, who, under the name of Pope Sylvester II, is looked upon as one of the great original thinkers of the Middle Ages. Gerbert had lectured for many years in the schools of France and attracted the attention of many of his contemporaries, finally becoming Archbishop of Rheims and then of Ravenna and eventually Pope. There is no doubt at all that he was the most distinguished scholar of his age and his writings show a range of interest and knowledge quite unparalleled in that generation. He lectured on astronomy at Rheims and in order to make his lecture clearer he constructed elaborate globes of the terrestrial and celestial spheres on which the courses of the planets were marked. Demonstration was his forte in teaching, and those who affect to condemn the *quadrivium* as an incomplete course of study founded only on book learning, should learn something of the methods employed in teaching it by Gerbert at the beginning of the last quarter of the tenth century. Besides the apparatus for demonstrations in astronomy he constructed an abacus for demonstrations in arithmetic and geometrical processes. This apparatus is said to have had twenty-seven divisions and a thousand counters of horn.

Every form of physical science interested him. His studies in astronomy led to some speculations with regard to light, but it was in sound that some of his best work was accomplished. He had an extraordinary knowledge of music for his time, and his letters contain many references to organs which he constructed. William of Malmesbury has incorporated into his chronicle a description of a magnificent musical instrument which was still to be seen in his day at Rheims and which was attributed to Gerbert's inventive and mechanical ability. The description of this organ seems to show that it was worked by steam. It is from a contemporary of Gerbert's that we learn that he had made a clock or sundial at Magdeburg which measured the hours very exactly and which was soon imitated in many parts of Europe. If we add to this account of his knowledge of science the fact that with Gerbert love for literature was a passion, and that probably his greatest claim to remembrance by posterity is the amount of labor and expense he devoted to gathering manuscripts of the classical authors, then some idea of the breadth of his intellectual sympathies will be realized.

Pope Silvester died in 1003. Before the end
of that century another pope who had gained
some distinction if not in science itself at least
by his connexion with the greatest medical school
of the time as a teacher and by his intimate
friendship with the great physicians who gave
Salerno its world-wide reputation, was to ascend
the papal throne. This was Victor III, who had
been for some time the Abbot of Monte Cassino
and who was suggested by the famous Pope
Gregory VII as one of the men most worthy to
succeed him. Desiderius as a younger man had
taught at Salerno, though it is not sure that he
actually taught medicine. At this time Salerno
had only a medical school and some courses in
philosophy in preparation for medicine. While
here Desiderius became the great personal friend
of Constantine Africanus, the greatest of the
Salernitan writers on medicine, and it was he
who persuaded Constantine to give up his teaching and devote himself in the Abbey at Monte
Cassino to writing out the account of all that he
had learned in medicine during his travels in the
East. Constantine spent the last thirty years
of his life in Monte Cassino doing this writing,
which has preserved the medicine of the preceding five hundred years for modern generations.
Another particular friend of Desiderius was
Alphanus, who taught medicine at Salerno for
many years and later became the Archbishop of
Salerno. Alphanus had been a monk at Monte
Cassino and had assisted Abbot Desiderius in

the foundation of the famous library there. We have two books on medicine that are attributed to him, *De Quattuor Elementis Corporis Humani,* and *De Unione Corporis et Animae,* as well as some smaller monographs. With Constantine and Alphanus as his very dear friends, it would seem that the tradition that Desiderius before becoming the Abbot of Monte Cassino had taught medicine should be accepted, and therefore we have another scientist to set among the popes. If not a scientist himself there is no doubt at all about his beneficent patronage of medicine.

These distinguished predecessors in the Chair of Peter in the immediately preceding centuries would make it still easier to understand the elevation of Peter of Spain to the papacy in spite of the fact that it seems incongruous to modern ideas that a physician should become pope. The opposition between science and faith which is so often suggested does not exist for the leaders of science in any period, not even our own, and the deeper a man's knowledge is the more profound is likely to be his persuasion, not only of the need of faith to balance human life, but likewise of the evidence for religious beliefs that accumulates in the course of a career devoted to science.

It must not be thought that we have been left to obtain information with regard to this physician who became pope from writers long after his time, who took the scattered traditions that might have been exaggerated by time and by the

unusualness of the conjunction of a knowledge
of medicine with an election to the papacy and
pieced them together as a marvel for posterity.
We have a number of mentions of this Pope and
his connexion with medicine made by contemporary writers. Martin of Oppavia mentions the
facts. Ptolemy of Lucca, who had been a con-
fessor of Thomas Aquinas and afterwards became Bishop of Toncelli, also calls attention to
them. Jacob da Voragine, Archbishop of Genoa,
the author of the *Legenda Aurea,* known also as
the *Speculum Sanctorum,* from which our American poet Longfellow borrowed the title and
some of the incidents for his *Golden Legend,*
also tells the story of the physician-pope. There
was a Dominican chronicler, Francisco Pippino,
of Bologna, best known perhaps for having
translated the original French version of Marco
Polo into Latin, who tells us with regard to Pope
John XXI that "he was more devoted to scientific questions than to the details of his duties
as a pope, and though he was a great philosopher
he found time for investigation and research in
the natural sciences."

It is easy to understand that many of these
men would be unsympathetic toward this interest
in the sciences. Especially was this true because
the Pope refused to give up his favorite studies
even after his elevation to the pontificate. There
is another side to this, however, which is very
interesting. When John became pope there had
been in recent years a great advance in scientific

knowledge and, as always happens when there
are new developments in natural science, many
discoveries seemed to contradict truths that had
been previously accepted on the authority of revelation. Pope John realized this and yet appreciated very well from his own knowledge of science that, while a little science might lead away
from faith, deeper knowledge of it presented no
dangers. He took advantage of his own scientific training, then, to point out that certain here-
sies which had arisen apparently on the basis of
new discoveries in science were worthy of condemnation because they perverted scientific truth
in order to make it apparently contradict Christian doctrine.

Peter, who was afterwards to be known as
Magister Petrus Hispanus and finally Pope John
XXI, was born, according to the best attainable
details, in the second decade of the thirteenth
century. His father had been a physician and
bore the name of Julius. Most of the writers
who mention him declare that he came from an
obscure family. He is one out of the many self-
made men of the thirteenth century, all of whom
rose through intellectual advantages. He seems
to have made his medical studies mainly in Paris,
though writers who are themselves interested in
Montpelier claim that he was also there for a
time, and it is not unlikely that the medical
schools of both these universities, which were so
celebrated at the time, attracted Peter who had
the renaissance spirit already awakened in him

of trying to exhaust all knowledge. While he was Pope he wrote a letter to the Bishop of Paris in which he congratulated himself on having been for many years, *per plurimos annos,* in the University of Paris. In this letter he asks particularly for certain doctrines that were being taught at Paris and were suspect of heresy, in order that he might be sure that nothing should injure the good name and the Catholic influence of his Alma Mater.

In this letter he confesses that he retains a special affection for Paris, because " within its dwellings he had been brought up from early years and had applied himself to various sciences, finding the opportunities provided for education most savory. After the deep draughts of knowledge there obtained, as far as the God of majesty, the Giver of true wisdom permitted him to take its opportunities, he does not think that he will ever be able to forget how much he owes to this mother of study." Sometime during the sixth decade of the thirteenth century, when he was probably about thirty-five years of age, Peter received an invitation to the chair of Physic, as medicine was then called, at the University of Siena in Italy. His salary was to be forty lire a year, which seems very small; but it is impossible to say what the value of money was at that time.

Just what sort of teaching in medicine Peter did in Siena we are not quite sure, though doubtless his little volume on eye diseases should be

taken as an index of the practical nature of his
instruction.   It serves to show that clinical observation held a large place in his method.   One
other thing seems sure.   During his time as professor of medicine at Siena this Italian town
passed the first law that we know of for the
regulation of public health.   That this was due
to Peter's influence we gather from the fact that
later on, when he was recalled to Rome, he was
made not only the Physician to the Pope but
moreover the Physician to the Papal City, under
the title of Archiater, an office that would about
correspond to that of Chief of the Department of
Health in our time.   This of course would stamp
him as a great benefactor of mankind in another
way, since after all it is the development of
sanitary science by means of public health regulations that has done so much to make the health
of communities better and to lower the death
rates of our cities.   It may seem surprising to
find the beginning of this in the thirteenth century, but it will not be so to those who know
how thoroughly the men of that time entered
into every phase of human thought and how
much that has proved enduring they accomplished
for the benefit of humanity.

While at Siena Peter did not confine himself
to medicine however, as indeed the great physicians of most progressive periods have not, but
devoted himself to philosophy as well as to medicine.   He wrote a little volume on logic known
by the name of the *Summulae Logicales* or Logic

Compendia, which became the text-book in this subject at most of the Italian universities during the next two centuries. This authorship has been disputed, mainly on the ground that it is too much to expect that a pioneer in medicine shall also be a leader in logic, but the investigation of the subject by Dr. Petella in his article in *Janus,* which we have already quoted, seems to leave no doubt that it was the same individual who wrote the little book on eye diseases and who taught physic at Siena, yet also was the author of this book on logic. It was this work on logic which indeed attracted Dante's attention to him more than anything else, since in his time it had come to be in the hands of most Italian students.

After this experience at Siena Peter seems to have returned to his native country, Portugal, and become the administrative head of the schools which existed there under the Archbishop of Lisbon. His success as an administrator in this position as well as the popularity he acquired as a teacher led to his appointment as Archdeacon of the Church of Braga. Subsequently he became Archbishop of Lisbon. A physician archbishop was not an anomaly, for many ecclesiastics of this time practised both medicine and surgery and became distinguished physicians. During this same thirteenth century we have the names and the works of many priests and monks who were also physicians. Among them is Gilles de Corbeil, a Benedictine

who afterwards became a Canon in Paris and
who made his contributions to medicine in verse.
We have the record of what are called poems by
him on the pulse, on the urine, and on drugs.
Then there was John of St. Amand, a Canon of
Tournai who was famous for his medical care
of the poor.   In England there was Richard of
Wendover, a Canon of St. Paul's, London.
Some of these clergymen-physicians rose to distinguished ecclesiastical positions.   Simon of
Genoa became the Chaplain of Pope Nicholas IV.   John of St. Giles, another Englishman,
became the theologian as well as the physician
to the French King Philip Augustus.   Odo, an
Abbot of St. Genevieve of Paris, was given the
title of physician as an honor.

Far from his ecclesiastical position then prov-
ing a detriment to his advancement, or his medical knowledge interfering with his ecclesiastical
preferment, the combination seems to have
proved, as Dr. Petella has pointed out, especially favorable to Peter of Spain.   The reputation which he had left behind him at Siena en-
dured, and after he had been made an Archbishop of Portugal he was summoned again to
Italy and became what we would now call con-
sulting physician to the Papal Court.   One of
the things that had especially rendered his memory enduring at Siena was his attention to public
health.   The title that was given him at Rome
was that of Archiater—Chief Physician—a title
that might well be taken to imply something of

that regulating relation which a chief health officer holds in our time. This title we know was confined to those who held positions at Royal Courts relating to public health and who sometimes had the duty of training those who had charge of public sanitation. It was while acting as Archiater already an Archbishop and probably a Cardinal, that Peter was made Pope and took the name John.

Peter's book on eye diseases, however, rather than himself and his career, are our special interest here. It must have attracted widespread attention and been much read, for in spite of the vicissitudes of time there are still some half a dozen manuscript copies of it in existence. There are books often considered more important of which we have fewer manuscripts. Of course his treatment of the subject of eye diseases was not as formal and regular as our modern text-books of this subject, but if we go over it a little we are able to get the hints of how Peter would have treated the subject in our formal way, had that been the custom of the time. It is quite possible to arrange the information he has under the divisions of anatomy, physiology, pathology, and treatment.

The initial sentence of the book—according to the custom of the times—is the invocation which we still use in such formal documents as wills, and which is to be found very commonly in all hospital and medical-college degrees, down even as late as Harvey's time: *In nomine Dei*

Amen.—In the name of God, Amen. The text
then opens logically with an account of the
anatomy of the eye.

Peter had much more information on the anatomy of the eye than perhaps we would be apt
to think that the doctors of his time possessed.
He says that the eye is composed of seven tunics
or layers, and three humors. Of the three
humors he calls what we now know as the
aqueous, the albugineous. The other two re-
fractive media bore in his time the names they
do now—the crystalline and vitreous bodies. In
his enumeration of the seven tunics or layers
of the eyeball he begins with the retina, and apparently had at least some vague idea of the fundamental importance of this layer for vision. In
this, however, it must be confessed that he simply
follows the order laid down by previous writers
on ophthalmology, especially the Arabs, who as
early as the ninth century named the coverings
of the eye this way. What he calls the secundine
tunic is the choroid, and then he mentions the
scliros (thus). The fourth tunic bears in his
enumeration the name of the tela aranea (the
spider-web), evidently in relation to the delicacy
of this tissue, and this undoubtedly refers to the
iris. The fifth tunic is the uvea, with the same
name as at present, and then there are, sixth and
seventh, the cornea and the conjunctiva, named
as now.

He then speaks of the muscles of the eye, and
asserts that each eye has eight. Six of them,

however, he calls lacerti, that is, reins or guiding ribbons for the eye. The other two external muscles which he refers to are evidently the elevator of the eyelid and the *orbicularis palpebrarum,* the sphincter muscle of the lids, which he includes among the eye muscles. He knows that the eye is spherical, for he speaks of it as "a noble round, radiating member." This last word, "radiating," gives us a hint as to his notion of the physiology of vision. In it is contained the groundwork of the old theory that there were visual radii or radiations which came out from the eye, this idea evidently depending on the radial manifestations which we see with regard to lights or bright objects. These radiations were, according to the philosophers of antiquity, supposed to originate in the eyes, to be reflected back from the objects and thus establish a contact, as it were, between the eye and the object, and therefore between the mind behind the eye and the object outside of it. This curious physiology of vision was developed much more fully after Peter's time.

Vision from another standpoint for Peter is nothing else than the crystalline humor. This phrase of his summed up another old physiological theory of vision that the images of objects were formed on the lens. A more metaphysical definition given by him is that "to see is the paradise of the soul, which goes out through the eyes as if through the bars of a prison"; and this paradise of the soul, the function of vision, is an intermediary between objects and the rational faculty, and it is because of this going-out of the soul that we are able to distinguish colors and figures.

What Peter has to say with regard to the pathology of the eye is more interesting to the modern ophthalmologist than his curious physiologic theories. He had a reasonably good idea of most of the eye diseases, and many details of information that are rather surprising for a period so long ago. He attributed crossed eyes to an affection of the eye muscles, but said that this was due to a defect of the brain. There were apparently some cases, however, in which he thought that the muscles alone were the cause of squint, while in others it was the nervous system. Evidently he knew something about both strabismus and ophthalmoplegia.

Pterygium, which, according to the habit of the time, Peter called *ungula* or nail, from a supposed resemblance to the shape of a finger nail, Peter mentions, but can only suggest applications of eel's blood for it. He mentions a form of blepharitis which he treats by the removal of the hairs, and the ashes of the leaves of the fig tree mixed with oil of bitter almonds. There is also an external application of this made of sweet oil, in which small lizards have been boiled. Lacrimal fistula Peter not only described, but he knew how difficult it was to treat, very probably from personal experience as well as the observations of others. He suggests the employ-

ment of exorcisms against it, on the principle
that, as has been suggested by Zanbrini, anything
that was so intractable as lacrimal fistula must
be the work of the devil and could only be improved by some means that would drive him out.
As noted by Dr. Petella in his article in *Janus,*
it was not until the beginning of the eighteenth
century that Anel at Turin gradually brought
to perfection the radical treatment of lacrimal
fistula.

It is with regard to certain internal eye diseases that Peter's knowledge is perhaps most
surprising. He describes cataract and has much
to say of it under the designation of water
" which descends into the eye." He sketches the
distinction between cataract which is produced
from without, traumatic cataract, and that which
arises spontaneously from internal causes. In
Peter's time they treated cataract by dislocation
of the lens by means of a needle made of gold or
silver. He does not make any mention of this,
however, and as the manuscript has come to us
in somewhat defective shape, this is thought to
be among the lost pages, for Peter does mention
the use of a needle for certain other things about
the eyes, and especially describes an operation
invented by himself for the treatment of trichi-
asis in which he cauterized the follicles of the
cilia with a gold or silver needle. After this
operation he bathed the eye with some " limara-
sicea water," a term which has quite confounded
the commentators, for there is no possible hint
of the composition of this external remedy.

Perhaps one of the most interesting suggestions in pathology that Peter makes is with regard to the hardening of the eye.   He describes
two forms of this.   One of them he calls *petro-
sitas* or *petrosezza* in the Italian manuscript, and
is explained later on by the word *tenebrosite*, or
a collection of humor in the pupil causing the
eye to become hard as stone.   By this term he
evidently means to designate an intense edema.
He describes a very different sort of hardness of
the eyes under another name, *durete,* which he
thinks a special disease coming from a natural
melancholy that the ordinary expulsive power of
nature is unable to dispose of.   Petella, who has
studied Peter's manuscript very carefully, is inclined to think that by the second form of hardness what we now call glaucoma is intended.
For the hardening of the eye due to edema Peter
recommended cathartic medicines, senna, aloes,
and various other purgatives.   He also recommends a better nutrition of the patient, with rest
while diluting whatever wine he takes.   For
what we would now call glaucoma he prescribes
fumigations with a decoction of acanthus mollis.
He recommends that all excesses in every way of
eating or *in Baccho* or *in Venere* must be
avoided.

In treatment Peter has many curious suggestions which the modern ophthalmologist would
find hard to understand.   Therapeutics in every
department is the curiosity of medical history.   We
are prone to think that the medieval physicians

were especially absurd in the remedies they employed for diseases of which they understood so little. It must not be forgotten, however, that it was left for a critic of our time to say that "modern physicians employed many remedies of which they knew nothing for diseases of which as a rule they knew less." Professor Richet, the distinguished director of the physiological laboratory, and professor of physiology at the University of Paris, in a recent article on "Medicine, Physicians and Medical Schools" in the important French magazine *La Revue Des Deux Mondes,* said that physicians must confess that it is in therapeutics always that our so-called science of medicine is weakest. At any time in history physicians who look back fifty years would be sure that most of the remedies which their colleagues of a half-century before had been giving were absurd. It seems not unlikely, he adds, that after fifty years many of the things that we are now doing for the treatment of disease will seem quite as absurd as those employed by our colleagues in the past.

Favorite lotions for the treatment of eye diseases suggested by John were solutions of sugar and of honey. This was a day when there were many ointments in all branches of surgery, so that it is not surprising that there are many different kinds of ointments for eye diseases. John's collyria nearly always had some bile in them, and also some white wine. The bile employed came from different animals according

as varying strength of ointment was supposed to
be needed. The bile of birds and especially of
the thrush and crane was supposed to be strong-
est. The bile of the fox and the dog, of the cat
and of the turtle-dove were also employed. This
very general use of bile or some extract of the
livers of animals or fishes for the treatment of
eye diseases seems to go back to Biblical times
when old Toby was cured by the gall of a fish,
which after being rubbed in for half an hour
" caused the whiteness of the eyes gradually to
disappear just as if one would remove the mem-
brane of an egg," as may be read in the book of
To¹·

A ꞁather curious remedy, apparently suggested
for many forms of conjunctival irritations and
inflammation, was the urine of infants. This
would seem extremely objectionable to us, and
yet one can not help but think that empirically
it might have proved soothing and that it may
be justified on scientific grounds. After all, the
urine of infants is usually a bland fluid not
strongly acid, and of such a specific gravity that it
would not set up osmotic processes in the eye.
It might, in the absence of a solution of boric
acid, be as soothing an eye-wash as could be
found. Infant urine very seldom contains bac-
teria, and rarely also contains any pathological
materials. It is just a solution of salts, of a specific gravity approaching that of blood. In the
olden times the idea of using it would seem much
less deterrent, because it was quite a common

practice for physicians to taste urine in order to determine whether it was sweet or had certain other qualities from which they might suspect certain pathological conditions.

With regard to another suggestion of Peter's, however, we can have nothing to say in extenuation. This was a filtered solution of human excrement in white wine. It represents another testimony to that curious tendency so commonly observed in human nature to make use of nauseating and offensive materials for therapeutic purposes. This has not completely died out in our time and any physician has notes of cases where excrementitious substances human or animal were used by even reasonably intelligent patients before coming for regular treatment. Ordure poultices are still used in country places.

As might be expected, Peter has some special remedies for styes. " Sure cures " for this affection have been so many and so curious that one is not surprised to find a queer suggestion in this old-time ophthalmologist. It was the body of ants, the head being removed, ground up and placed on the eyelids. This was guaranteed to cure. On the other hand, some of the remedies have quite a familiar modern air—for instance, purgation was one of the things suggested where styes occurred frequently, and the substance recommended for this purpose seems to have been our cascara sagrada.

For various forms of conjunctivitis the white of egg was employed, and for hemorrhages into the conjunctiva a mixture of honey and the white of egg was especially recommended. As we have said, however, bile and preparations made from the livers of animals and fumigations with the smoke of burning liver were perhaps the most important remedies suggested in the ophthalmology of this kind.   This might seem utterly absurd, and yet Dr. Petella, in discussing this subject, does not think so, and he refers to various recent authorities in ophthalmology who have reverted to some of these old practices in the use of fumigations with the livers of animals and whose experience shows that probably the medieval ophthalmologist was not so ridiculous as we might think.

One of the most interesting features of Peter's book is the authors he quotes in confirmation of various ideas and from whom he borrows the details of pathology and treatment. He confesses his obligations especially to Theodore, who was probably a physician of the Emperor Frederick II during the first half of the thirteenth century.   Theodore was Peter's special master and patron.   Peter seems to have known the old authors pretty well, for he quotes Plato and Hippocrates's aphorisms with regard to the eye.   Avicenna is quoted among the more modern writers, and Constantine Africanus, the celebrated teacher of medicine at Salerno, the greatest writer of medicine of the eleventh century, who retired to the monastery at Monte Cassino and became a monk in order to have the time and leisure to complete the dozen of folio volumes on medicine that are attributed to him. The medical authority to whom Peter most often refers is Galen, who was the most read medical author during all the Middle Ages, and who dominated medical thought for more than a thousand years. Of his contemporaries, two, Anselmo of Giovino and William of Salicet, the celebrated Italian surgeon of the time, who was the first to introduce case histories into his textbook on surgery, are probably the only ones to be mentioned. William was undoubtedly the greatest genius in surgery of his century. Prof. Clifford Allbutt, in his address on " Medicine and Surgery Down to the Sixteenth Century," at St. Louis in 1904, placed him on a lofty pinnacle when he declared that he had suggested the advisability of trying to obtain union by first intention.

Peter borrowed some remedies from the school of Salerno, and especially from Bienvenu Grasse or Graphée of Jerusalem, whose book, the *Ars Probata de Ægritudinibus Oculorum,* was one of the best known treatises on eye diseases in the twelfth century. Curiously enough, Bienvenu and Peter of Spain are quoted in certain passages together by Guy de Chauliac in his *Chirurgia Magna.* Guy was the father of modern surgery, and there was little that was of any value in the writers preceding his time that he did not collect into his book. Unfortunately, however, he rejected William of Salicet's idea of union by first intention, and it is to him that we owe the teaching of the necessity for pus formation in most cases if union is to be secured. In a word, Peter's little book, its citations from predecessors and its quotations by workers in medicine who came after its author, is a central point from which the history of some four or five medical centuries may be viewed to advantage.

The surprise of the book and the incidents connected with it is, of course, that the leading ophthalmologist of an important century in medical history should have been chosen as pope. The ordinarily accepted ideas as to the relations of the popes to science would not lead us to expect anything like this. All the distinguished physicians and surgeons of the centuries from the tenth to the fifteenth, except, of course, the Arabs, were clergymen. The men whom we have mentioned here in connexion with Peter's book, Constantine Africanus, William of Salicet, Lanfranc, the great leader of surgery and anatomy in Paris, and Guy de Chauliac, the father of modern surgery, were all ecclesiastics who had taken at least minor orders, and some of the physicians and surgeons like Peter himself reached high ecclesiastical preferment. The papal physicians, that is the official medical attendants of the popes, in these centuries, so far as we know them, are among the greatest contributors to medical science and include many of the names best known in medical history. The medical school at Bologna was in the Papal States for several centuries at the height of its fame, and probably the greatest investigating medical school, the one in which, to use a very modern phrase, intensive research was the watchword of the faculty, was the Papal Medical School at Rome, in which such men as Columbus, the discoverer of the circulation of the blood in the lungs; Eustachius, of tubal fame; Varolius, after whom the Pons is named; Caesalpinus, to whom the Italians attribute the discovery of the circulation of the blood before Harvey; Malpighi, whose name is attached to more structures in the human body than any other — were the great teachers.

The more we know in definite details about these early times the less does the complacent impression remain that ours are the only generations that have ever done serious work in medicine or in science.   In gathering material for a book on *The Popes and Science,* recently published by the Fordham University Press,[3] what I had particularly called to my attention was the immense amount of knowledge which had been gained in the past and then lost through some neglect or through some turning of attention to other subjects.   Certainly the Universities of the thirteenth century, and above all, the medical schools which required three years of preliminary study and four years of medicine before a degree was given, and a fifth year if surgery was to be practised, deserve anything but contempt, and make us realize that instead of advancing we have only too often retrograded.

[3] Fordham University Press, New York, 1908.

IV.

GUY DE CHAULIAC, FATHER OF MODERN SURGERY.

ORIGINAL! move onward in your
        pride,—
Oh! how the spirit would sink morti-
        fied,
Could you but know that long ago,
All thoughts whatever dull or clever,
That across the twilight of your brain,
Have been o'er and o'er again
Occupying other men.—
                    GOETHE: *Faust.*

WE have now before us a view
    of the powers of man of the
earliest point to which we can trace
written history, and what strikes us
most is how very little his nature or
abilities have changed in seven thousand years; what he admired we admire; what were his limits in fine
handiwork are also ours. We may
have a wider outlook, a greater under-
standing of things, our interests may
have extended in this interval; but as
far as human nature and tastes go,
man is essentially unchanged in this
interval.—FLINDERS PETRIE, *The
Romance of Early Civilization.*

IS there anything whereof it may
    be said,
    See this is new?
It hath been already of old time
    Which was before us.
There is no remembrance of former
        things;
Neither shall there be any remembrance
    Of things that are to come
With those that shall come hereafter.

GUY DE CHAULIAC.

GUY DE CHAULIAC,

FATHER OF MODERN SURGERY

SURGERY is usually supposed to be almost entirely a development of the practical scientific genius of the last few generations. Some attempts man had to make of course at treating by means of the knife what would otherwise be absolutely hopeless cases, even before the nineteenth century, but such attempts, we are inclined to think, lacked scientific precision to a great extent, and were wanting in that skilful application of anatomical knowledge and mechanical principles which have made surgery such an important specialty in recent years. This impression with regard to surgery is only a little more emphatic than a corresponding feeling very generally entertained with regard to science of all kinds. Most people are prone to think that only in the nineteenth century did men come to serious thoughts about science, meaning by that term, classified knowledge of physical nature. Nothing could well be less true, and if surgery may be taken as the symbol of the untruth of the propositions suggested, then it is comparatively easy to show how much men were interested in science six or seven centuries ago, and how much they accomplished in developing their knowledge *and applying it.*

The immediate evidence of the value of old-time surgery is to be found in the fact that Guy de Chauliac, who is commonly spoken of in the history of medicine as the Father of Modern Surgery, lived his seventy-odd years of life during the fourteenth century, and accomplished the best of his work therefore about five centuries before surgery in our modern sense of the term is supposed to have developed. A glance at his career, however, will show how old are most of the important developments of surgery, also in what a thoroughly scientific temper of mind this subject was approached more than a century before the close of the Middle Ages. The life of this French surgeon, indeed, who was a cleric and occupied the position of chamberlain and physician-in-ordinary to three of the Avignon Popes, is not only a contradiction of many of the traditions as to the backwardness of our medieval forbears in medicine, that are readily accepted by many presumably educated people, but it is the best possible antidote for that insistent misunderstanding of the Middle Ages which attributes profound ignorance of science, almost complete failure of observation, and an absolute lack of initiative in applications of science, to the men of those times.

Guy de Chauliac's life is modern in nearly every phase. He was educated in a little town in the south of France, made his medical studies at Montpelier, and then went on a journey of nearly a thousand miles into Italy, in order to make his post-graduate studies. Italy occupied the place

in science at that time that Germany has taken
during the nineteenth century, and a young man
who wanted to get into touch with the great
masters in medicine naturally went down into the
Peninsula. Traditions as to the opposition of
the Church to science notwithstanding, Italy,
which was more completely under the influence
of the popes and ecclesiastics than any other
country in Europe, continued to be the home of
post-graduate work in science for the next four
centuries. Almost needless to say, the journey
to Italy was more difficult of accomplishment
and involved more expense and time than would
even the voyage from America in our time.
Chauliac realized, however, that both time and
expense would be well rewarded, and his ardor
for the rounding-out of his education was amply
recompensed by the event.

Even this post-graduate experience in Italy
did not satisfy him, for after having studied
several years with the most distinguished Italian
teachers of anatomy and surgery, he spent some
time in Paris, so as to be sure that he would be
acquainted with the best that was being done
in his specialty in every part of the world. He
then settled down to his own life-work, carrying his Italian and French masters' teachings
well beyond the point where he received them,
and after years of personal experience, he gathered together his masters' ideas, tested by his
own observations, into his *Chirurgia Magna,* a
great text-book of surgery, which sums up the

subject succinctly, yet completely, for succeeding generations. When we talk about what he
accomplished for surgery, we are not dependent
on traditions nor vague information gleaned
from contemporaries and successors, who might
perhaps have been so much impressed by his personality as to be hampered in their critical judgment of him. We know the man in his surgical
works and they have continued to be classics in
surgery ever since. It is an honorable distinction
for the medicine of the fourteenth, fifteenth,
and sixteenth centuries that Guy de Chauliac's
book was the most read volume of the time in
medicine. Evidently the career of such a man
is of import, not alone to physicians but to all
who are interested in the history of education.

Chauliac derives his name from the little town
of Chauliac in the diocese of Mende, almost in
the center of what is now the department of
Lozère. The records of births and deaths were
not considered so important in the fourteenth
century as they are now, and so we are not sure
of either, in the case of Chauliac. It is usually
considered that he was born some time during
the last decade of the thirteenth century, probably toward the end of it, and that he died about
1370. Of his early education we know nothing,
but it must have been reasonably efficient, since
it gave him a good knowledge of Latin, which
was the universal language of science and especially of medicine at that time; and though his
own style, as must be expected, is no better than

that of his contemporaries, he knew how to express his thoughts clearly in straightforward Latin, with only such a mixture of foreign terms as his studies suggested and the exigencies of a new development in science almost required. Later in life he seems to have known Arabic very well, for he is evidently familiar with Arabian books and does not depend merely on translations of them.

Pagel, in his first volume of Puschmann's Handbook of the History of Medicine,[1] who is conceded to be the best living authority on the history of medicine, says, on the authority of Nicaise and others, that Chauliac probably received his early education from the village clergyman. His parents were poor, and but for ecclesiastical interest in him, it would have been difficult for him to obtain his education. The Church supplied for that time the foundations and scholarships, home and traveling, of our day, and Chauliac was amongst the favored ones. How well he deserved the favor his subsequent career shows, as it completely justifies the judgment of his patrons. He went first to Toulouse, as we know from his affectionate mention of one of his teachers there. Toulouse was more famous for law, however, than for medicine, and after a time Chauliac sought Montpelier to complete his medical studies.

For English-speaking people an added interest

[1] Puschmann, *Handbuch der Geschichte der Medizin.* Fischer: Jena. 1902.

in Guy de Chauliac will be the fact that one of his teachers at Montpelier was Bernard Gordon, very probably a Scotchman, who taught for some thirty-five years at this famous University in the south of France, and died near the end of the first quarter of the fourteenth century. One of Chauliac's fellow-students at Montpelier was John of Gaddesden, the first English Royal Physician by official appointment of whom we have any account. John is mentioned by Chaucer in his *Doctor of Physic,* and is usually looked upon as one of the fathers of English medicine. Chauliac did not think much of him, though his reason for his dislike of him will probably be somewhat startling to those who assume that the men of the Middle Ages always clung to authorities. Chauliac's objection to Gaddesden's book is that he merely repeats his masters and does not dare to think for himself. It is not hard to understand that such an independent thinker as Chauliac should have been utterly dissatisfied with a book that did not go beyond the forefathers in medicine that it quotes: This is the significant explanation of his well-known expression, " Last of all arose the scentless rose of England (*Rosa Angliae* was the name of John of Gaddesden's book,[2]) in which, on its being sent

[2] They affected poetical titles for medical works in those days, and we have the *Lilium Medicinae,* the *Flos Medicinae,* and other names for books which it would be very hard to recognize as serious treatises. This curious custom in nomenclature was not confined

to me, I hoped to find the odor of sweet originality, but instead of that I encountered only the
fictions of Hispanus, of Gilbert, and of The-
odoric." The presence of a Scotch professor
and an English fellow-student, afterwards a
Royal Physician at Montpelier at the beginning
of the fourteenth century, shows how much more
cosmopolitan was life in those times than we are
prone to think, and what attraction for men from
long distances a great medical university possessed.

After receiving his degree of Doctor of Medicine at Montpelier, Chauliac went, as we have
said, to Bologna. Here he attracted the attention and received the special instruction of Bertruccio, who was attracting students from all
over Europe at this time and was making some
excellent demonstrations in anatomy by means
of dissections. Chauliac tells of the methods
that Bertruccio used in order that bodies might
be in as good condition as possible for demonstration purposes, and mentions the fact that he
saw him do many dissections in different ways.

In Roth's life of Vesalius which is usually
considered one of the most authoritative medical
historical works not only with regard to the details of Vesalius's life, but also in all that concerns anatomy about and for some centuries

to medieval books, however, for some of the titles
even of the law tomes were couched in this botanical
fashion, and even more common-place books had the
same distinction.

before that time, there is a passage quoted from
Chauliac himself which shows how freely dissection was practised at the Italian Universities
in the fourteenth century. This passage deserves to be quoted at some length because there
are even serious historians who still cite a bull
of Pope Boniface VIII, issued in 1300, forbid-
ding the boiling and dismembering of bodies in
order to transport them to long distances for
burial in their own country, as being, either
rightly or wrongly, interpreted as a prohibition
of dissection and therefore preventing the development of anatomy. In the notes to his history of dissection during this period in Bologna
Roth says: " Without doubt the passage in Guy
de Chauliac which tells of having frequently
seen dissections, must be considered as referring
to Bologna. This passage runs as follows: ' My
master, Bertruccius, conducted the dissection
very often after the following manner: the dead
body having been placed upon a bench, he used
to make four lessons on it. In the first, the nu-
tritional portions were treated, because they are
so likely to become putrified. In the second, he
demonstrated the spiritual members; in the third,
the animate members; in the fourth, the ex-
tremities.' " [3]

Bertruccio's master, Mondino, is hailed in the
history of medicine as the father of dissection.
His book on dissection was for the next three

[3] Roth, *Andreas Vesalius*. Basel, 1896.

centuries in the hands of nearly every medical
scholar in Europe who was trying to do good
work in anatomy. It was not displaced until
Vesalius came as the great father of modern
anatomy who revolutionized the science in the
Renaissance time. Mondino had devoted himself to the subject with unfailing ardor and enthusiasm, and from everywhere in Europe the
students came to receive inspiration in his dis-
secting-room. Within a few years such was the
enthusiasm for dissection aroused by him in
Bologna that there were many legal prosecutions
for body-snatching, the consequence doubtless
of a regulation of the Medical Department of the
University of Bologna, that if the students
brought a body to any of their teachers he was
bound to dissect it for them. Bertruccio, Mondino's disciple and successor, continued this great
work, and now Chauliac, the third in tradition,
was to carry the Bolognese methods back to
France, and his position as chamberlain to the
Pope was to give them a wide vogue throughout
the world. The great French surgeon's attitude
toward anatomy and dissection can be judged
from his famous expression that " the surgeon
ignorance of anatomy carves the human body as
a blind man carves wood." The whole subject
of dissection at this time has been widely discussed in the first three chapters of my *Popes
and Science,* where those who are interested in
the matter may follow it to their satisfaction.

After his Bologna experience Chauliac went

to Paris. Evidently his indefatigable desire to
know all that there was to be known would not
be satisfied until he had spent some time at the
great French University where Lanfranc, after
having studied under William of Salicet in Italy,
had gone to establish that tradition of French
surgery which was to maintain Frenchmen as
the leading surgeons of the world until the nineteenth century. Lanfranc, himself an Italian, had
been called to Paris to teach because the faculty
realized that they needed the inspiration of the
Italian movement in surgery for the establish-
ment of a good school of surgery in connexion
with the University. The teaching so well begun
by Lanfranc had been magnificently continued
by Mondeville, and Chauliac was fortunate
enough to come under the influence of Petrus
de Argentaria, who was worthily maintaining
the tradition of practical teaching in anatomy and
surgery which had been so well founded by his
great predecessors of the thirteenth century.
After this grand tour, Chauliac was prepared to
do work of the highest order, for he had been in
touch with all that was best in the medicine and
surgery of his time.

Like many another distinguished member of his
profession, Chauliac did not settle down in the
scene of his ultimate labors at once, but was
something of a wanderer. His own words are,
" Et per multa tempora operatus fui in multis
partibus." Perhaps out of gratitude to the clerical patrons of his native town to whom he owed

so much, or because of his obligations to his
bishop, he practised first in his native diocese
of Mende; thence he removed to Lyons, where
we know that he was for several years, for in
1344 he took part as a canon in a chapter that
met in the Church of St. Just in that city. When
precisely he was called to Avignon we do not
know, though when the Black Death ravaged that
city in 1348, he was the body physician of Pope
Clement VI, who spoke of him as " venerabilis
et circumspectus vir, dominus Guido de Cauliaco,
canonicus et praepositus ecclesiae Sancto Justi
Lugduni, medicusque domini Nostri Papae." All
the rest of his life was passed in the papal
capital. He served as chamberlain-physician to
three Popes, Clement VI, Innocent VI and Urban
V. We do not know the exact date of his death,
but when Pope Urban V went to Rome in 1367,
Chauliac was putting the finishing touches on his
Chirurgia Magna, which, as he tells us, was un-
dertaken as a *solatium senectutis*. When Urban
returned to Avignon for a time in 1370, Chauliac
was dead. His life-work is summed up for us
in this great treatise on surgery, full of anticipations in surgical procedures that we are prone
to think much more modern.

Chauliac's right to the title of father of surgery will perhaps be best appreciated from the
brief account of his recommendations as to the
value of surgical intervention for conditions in
the three most important cavities of the body,
the skull, the thorax, and the abdomen. These

cavities have usually been the dread of surgeons. Chauliac not only used the trephine, but laid down very exact indications for its application. Expectant treatment was to be the rule in wounds of the head, yet when necessary, interference was counseled as of great value. His prognosis of brain injuries was much better than that of his predecessors. He says that he has seen injuries to the brain, followed by some loss of brain substance, yet with recovery of the patient. In one case that he notes a considerable amount of brain substance was lost, yet the patient recovered with only a slight defect of memory and even this disappeared after a time. He lays down exact indications for the opening of the thorax, that *noli me tangere* of surgeons at all times, even our own, and points out the relations of the ribs and the diaphragm so as to show just where the opening should be made in order to remove fluid of any kind.

In abdominal conditions, however, Chauliac's anticipation of modern views is most surprising. He recognized that wounds of the intestines were surely fatal unless leakage could be prevented. Accordingly he suggested the opening of the abdomen and the sewing up of such intestinal wounds as could be located. He describes a method of suture for these cases and even invented a needle-holder. To most people it would seem absolutely out of the question that such surgical procedures could be practised in the fourteenth century. We have the definite record of them, however, in a text-book that was the most read volume on the subject for several centuries. Some of the surprise with regard to these operations will vanish when it is realized that during the thirteenth century in Italy a method of anesthesia by means of opium and mandragora was in common use, having been invented by Ugo da Luca, and Chauliac must not only have known of it but must have employed it frequently. We have nothing from him directly bearing on this subject, but then even in our own time surgeons do not discuss anesthesia, but assume a knowledge of it.

Many people might be prone to think that the hospitals of Chauliac's time would not be suitable for such surgical work as he describes. It is, however, only another amusing assumption of this self-complacent age of ours to think that we were the first who ever made hospitals worthy of the name. As a matter of fact the old-time hospitals were even better than ours or as a rule better than any we had until the present generation. In *The Popes and Science* [4] in the chapter on " The Foundation of City Hospitals " I call attention to the fact that architects of the present-day go back to the hospitals of the Middle Ages in order to find the models for hospitals for the modern times. Mr. Arthur Dillon, a well-known New York architect, writing of a hospital built in France toward the end of the thirteenth century says:

[4] Fordham University Press, 1908.

It was an admirable hospital in every way, *and it is doubtful if we to-day surpass it.* It was isolated; the ward was separated from the other buildings; it had the advantage we so often lose of being but one story high, and more space was given to each patient than we can now afford.

The ventilation by the great windows and ventilators in the ceiling was excellent; it was cheerfully lighted, and the arrangement of the gallery shielded the patients from dazzling light and from draughts from the windows and afforded an easy means of supervision, while the division by the roofless, low partitions isolated the sick and obviated the depression that comes from the sight of others in pain.

It was, moreover, in great contrast to the cheerless white wards of to-day. The vaulted ceiling was very beautiful; the woodwork was richly carved, and the great windows over the altars were filled with colored glass. Altogether, it was one of the best examples of the best period of Gothic architecture.[5]

This was but one of many. Virchow in his article on Hospitals quoted in the same chapter [6] calls atention to the fact that in the thirteenth and fourteenth centuries every town of 5,000 or

[5] The Altar in these hospitals was placed at the end of a ward or between two wards, or, as may be seen in the famous old hospital at Milan, at the intersection of long wards, so that all the patients, even those confined to bed, could hear Mass on Sunday morning. This arrangement, as can be easily understood, afforded great consolation to patients, and yet the very openness of construction required for this made ventilation very efficient. In countries where the winters are not severe, this was after all the principal purpose in the construction of a hospital.

[6] *The Popes and Science.*

more inhabitants had its hospital, founded on the model of the great Santo Spirito Hospital in Rome, and all of them did good work. The surgeons of Guy de Chauliac's time would indeed find hospitals wherever they might be called in consultation, even in small towns, much more numerous and as a rule at least as well organized as our own.[7]

It is no wonder that with such a good hospital organization excellent surgery was accomplished.

Hernia was Chauliac's specialty, and in it his surgical judgment is admirable. He did not hesitate to say that many operations for hernia in his time were done not for the benefit of the patient but for the benefit of the surgeon,—a remark that will strike a sympathetic cord in many medical minds even at the present time. His rule was that a truss should be worn, and

[7] Even here in America the hospitals erected by the Spaniards early in the sixteenth century were much better than anything we had at any time in what is now the United States until near the end of the nineteenth century. Prescott, in his *History of the Conquest of Mexico,* Vol. I, page 48, says: " I must not forget to notice here an institution the introduction of which in the Old World is ranked among the beneficent fruits of Christianity. Hospitals were established in the principal cities, for the cure of the sick and the permanent refuge of the disabled soldier, and surgeons were placed over them, who were so far better than those in Europe, says an old chronicler, that they did not protract the cure, in order to increase the pay." Some of these hospitals were very handsome buildings, and one erected by Cortez in the City of Mexico in 1532, still in existence, is one of the finest hospitals of all time.

no operation attempted unless the patient's life
was endangered by the hernia. It is to him that
we owe the invention of the method of taxis, or
manipulation of a hernia, to bring about its reduction, which was in use until the end of the
nineteenth century. He suggested that trusses
could not be made according to rule, but must
be adapted to each individual case. He invented
several forms of truss himself, and in general
it may be said that his manipulative skill and his
power to apply mechanical principles to his work
are the most characteristic of his qualities. This
is particularly noteworthy in his chapters on fractures and dislocations, in which he suggests
various methods of reduction and realizes very
practically the mechanical difficulties that were to
be encountered in the correction of the deformi-
ties due to these pathological conditions. In a
word, we have a picture of the skilled surgeon
of the modern time in this treatise of a four-
teenth-century surgeon.

Chauliac's book is confessedly a compilation.
He has taken the good wherever he found it,
though he adds, modestly enough, that " his work
also contains whatever his own measure of intelligence enabled him to find useful (*quae juxta
modicitatem mei ingenii utilia reputavi*)." Indeed it is the critical judgment displayed by Chauliac in selecting from his predecessors that best illustrates at once the practical character of his
intellect and his discerning spirit. What the men
of his time are said to have lacked is the critical

faculty. They were encyclopedic in intellect and gathered all kinds of information without discrimination, is the common criticism of medieval writers. No one can say this of Chauliac, however, and above all he was no respecter of authority, merely for the sake of authority. His criticism of John of Gaddesden's book shows that the blind following of those who had gone before was his special *bête noire*. His bitterest reproach for many of his predecessors was that " they followed one another like cranes, whether for love or fear, he would not say."

It must not be thought, however, that it was only with the coarser applications of surgery that Chauliac concerned himself. He was very much interested in the surgical treatment of eye diseases and wrote a monograph on cataract, in which he gathers what was known before his time and discusses it in the light of his own experience. The writing of such a book is not so surprising at this time if we recall that in the preceding century the famous Pope John XXI, who had been a physician before he became pope, and under the name of Peter of Spain was looked up to as one of the distinguished scientists of his time, had written a book on eye diseases that has recently been the subject of much attention.

Pope John, as we saw in the sketch of him preceding this, had much to say of cataract, dividing it into traumatic and spontaneous, and probably suggesting the needling of cataract, a gold needle being used for the purpose. Chauliac's method of treating cataract was by depression. His care in the selection of patients may be appreciated from his treatment of John of Luxemburg, King of Bavaria, blind from cataract, who consulted Chauliac in 1336 while on a visit to Avignon with the King of France. Chauliac refused to operate, however, and put off the king with dietary regulations.[8]

The more one reads of Chauliac's work the less is one surprised at the estimation in which he has been held wherever known. Modern writers on the history of medicine have all been enthusiastic in their admiration of him just in proportion to the thoroughness of their acquaintance with him. Portal, in his *History of Anatomy and Surgery,* says: " Finally, it may be averred that Guy de Chauliac said nearly everything which modern surgeons say and that his work is of infinite price, but unfortunately too little read, too little pondered." Malgaigne declares Chauliac's *Chirurgia Magna,* " a masterpiece of learned and luminous writing." Professor Clifford Allbutt, who is the Regius Professor of Physic at the University of Cambridge, says of Chauliac's treatise: " This great work I have studied carefully and not without prejudice; yet

[8] John's fate may be recalled. At the Battle of Crecy ten years later, by his command, his squires tied his bridle rein to theirs and with sword in hand, the heroic old man rushed into the thickest of the fight and met the fate of so many others on the French side, who fell before the sturdy English yeomen of Edward III.

I cannot wonder that Fallopius compared the author to Hippocrates or that John Freind calls him the Prince of Surgeons. It is rich, aphoristic, orderly and precise." [9]

Julius Pagel in Puschmann's *Handbook of the History of Medicine,* says: "Chauliac represents the summit of attainment in medieval surgery and laid the foundation of that primacy in surgery which the French maintained down to the nineteenth century."

If to this account of his professional career it be added that Chauliac's personality is, if possible, more interesting than his surgical accomplishment, some idea of the significance of the life of the great father of modern surgery will be realized. We have already quoted the distinguished words of praise accorded him by Pope Clement VI. That they were well deserved, Chauliac's conduct during the black death which ravaged Avignon in 1348, shortly after his arrival in the papal city, would have been sufficient of itself to attest. The occurrence of the plague in a city usually gave rise to an exhibition of the most arrant cowardice, and all who could, fled. In many of the European cities the physicians joined the fugitives, and the ailing were left to care for themselves. With a very few exceptions, this was the case at Avignon, but Guy was among those who remained faithful to his duty and took

[9] *The Historical Relations of Medicine and Surgery,* by T. Clifford Allbutt, M.A., M.D., London: Macmillan & Co. Ltd. 1905.

on himself the self-sacrificing labor of caring for the sick, doubly harassing because so many of his brother-physicians were absent. He denounces their conduct as shameful, yet does not boast of his own courage, but on the contrary says that he was in constant fear of the disease. Toward the end of the epidemic he was attacked by the plague and for a time his life was despaired of. Fortunately he recovered, to become the most influential among his colleagues, the most higly admired of the physicians of his generation, and the close personal friend of all the high ecclesiastics, who had witnessed his magnificent display of courage and of helpfulness for the plague-stricken during the epidemic. He wrote a very clear account of the epidemic, which leaves no doubt that it was true bubonic plague.

After this fine example Chauliac's advice to brother-physicians in the specialty of surgery carried added weight. In the introductory chapter of his *Chirurgia Magna* he said:

The surgeon should be learned, skilled, ingenious, and of good morals. Be bold in things that are sure, cautious in dangers; avoid evil cures and practices; be gracious to the sick, obliging to his colleagues, wise in his predictions. Be chaste, sober, pitiful, and merciful; not covetous nor extortionate of money; but let the recompense be moderate, according to the work, the means of the sick, the character of the issue or event and its dignity.

No wonder that Malgaigne says of him:

Never since Hippocrates has medicine heard such language filled with so much nobility and so full of matter in so few words.

Chauliac was in every way worthy of his great contemporaries and the period in which his lot was cast. Ordinarily we are not apt to think of the early fourteenth century as an especially productive period in human history, but such it is. Dante's *Divine Comedy* was entirely written during Chauliac's life. Petrarch was born within a few years of Chauliac himself, Boccaccio in Italy, and Chaucer in England, did their writing while Chauliac was still alive. There are few centuries in history that can show the existence of so many men whose work was to have an enduring influence for all the aftertime, as this upon which Chauliac's career shed so bright a light. The preceding century had seen the origin of the Universities and the rise of such supremely great men as Albertus Magnus, Roger Bacon, Thomas Aquinas, and the other great scholars of the early days of the Mendicant Orders, and had made the intellectual mould of university training in which men's minds for seven centuries were to be formed, so that Chauliac, instead of being an unusual phenomenon is only a fitting expression of the interest of this time in everything, including the physical sciences and, above all, medicine and surgery.

For some people it may be a source of surprise that Chauliac should have had the intellectual training to enable him to accomplish such judicious work in his specialty. Many people will be apt to assume that he accomplished what he did in spite of his training. Genius does its own work, even in an unfavorable environment, and notwithstanding educational disadvantages. Those who would be satisfied with any such explanation, however, know nothing of the educational opportunities provided in the period of which Chauliac was the fruit. He is a typical university man of the beginning of the fourteenth century, and the universities must be given due credit for him. It is ordinarily assumed that the universities paid very little attention to science and that a scientist would find practically nothing to satisfy in their curricula. Let Professor Huxley be the witness for the complete contradiction of any such opinion. In his address on Universities Actual and Ideal, delivered as the Rectorial Address at Aberdeen University in 1874, he expressed himself in terms very different from what would ordinarily be expected from so thorough-going a modern scientist. His opinion may be found in the quotation near the beginning of the sketch of Albertus Magnus. Here we need only repeat his expression:

> I doubt if the curriculum of any modern university shows so clear and generous a comprehension of what is meant by culture as this old Trivium and Quadrivium does.

In the light of Chauliac's life it is indeed amusing to read the excursions of certain historians into the relationship of the Popes and the Church to science during the Middle Ages. Chauliac is typically representative of medieval science, a man who gave due weight to authority, yet tried everything by his own experience and who sums up in himself such wonderful advance in surgery that during the last twenty years the students of the history of medicine have been more interested in him than in anyone who comes during the intervening six centuries. Chauliac, however, instead of meeting with any opposition, encountered encouragement, liberal patronage, generous interest, and even enjoyed the intimate friendship of the highest ecclesiastics and of the popes of his time. In every way his life may be taken as a type of what we have come to know about the Middle Ages, when we study them close up, and in the lives of the men who counted for most in them, and do not accept merely the broad generalizations which are always likely to be deceptive and which in the past have deceived men into the most absurd and ridiculous notions with regard to a wonderful period in human history.

V.

REGIOMONTANUS, ASTRONOMER
AND BISHOP.

"THUS I think I have my being upon this terrestrial orbe which is both situate and as it were thrust out at vast distance from the glorious region of light and life, and likewise in a continual flux and reflux in all and every of its parts. Nor doe I only live upon it, but weare also a body that is made up of the grosse and vile parts thereof, and is necessarily determined to that suddain change and dissolution whereunto the laws of its constitution have subjected the whole.

"But nevertheless I have an intellectual nature, which incessantly aspires after another and that a more happy state of being, and besides its knowledge of a future happiness is furnished with faculties suited to the attainment thereof, if in compliance with the revealed will of God in Christ, and the innate laws of its owne originall purity it shall vanquish the irregular suggestions of my body, to which for a while it is coupled : and managing both its selfe, and that, under a due obedience to that will and those laws, shall employ the utmost faculties of both in adoring the supreme and ineffable being, in the practicing of virtue, and in doing good to men."— SYDENHAM: *Preface to "Observationes Medicæ."*

THE truths of natural science continually approach nearer those of religion, so that at last both must be united in the most intimate connexion.—OERSTED.

REGIOMONTANUS.

MOST of us have forgotten many of the details of the landing of Columbus on these American shores; but very probably nearly all of us recall the episode of the eclipse of the moon which occurred not long after his landing, and which the great navigator used to such decided advantage in influencing the minds of the natives favorably to himself and his party. According to the story, the Indians had been quite ready at first to welcome the strangers who came in the white-winged vessels from over-seas, and whom they were inclined to think of as having come down from heaven; a false impression which the Spaniards were at no pains to remove, since it made the natives only the more ready to accomplish all their visitors' wishes. It was not long, however, before the conduct of the Spaniards showed even the credulous savages that their visitors were very human, and as a consequence their respect for the strangers began to decline. They became much less generous in their proffers of assistance. and even showed some signs of disaffection and of a desire for their visitors to depart. This disaffection at length increased to such a degree that some of the Spaniards began to fear for the safety of the expedition.

It was then that Columbus's knowledge of astronomy came to the aid of himself and his companions. Recalling that a lunar eclipse was due in a few days, he foretold its occurrence to the wondering savages. According to tradition, his method of telling it was not strictly scientific; it followed rather the mode of expression best suited to the intelligence and mental habits of the people whom he was addressing. He declared that after a few nights they would see a huge monster come to devour the moon. The reason he assigned for this catastrophe was that the Great Spirit, dissatisfied with their ill treatment of His messengers, the Spaniards, would send the monster to deprive this ungrateful people of the beneficent luminary they had hitherto enjoyed at night.

Pursuant to his statement, on the very night and at the very hour foretold the moon began to disappear gradually in the jaws apparently of a monster, whose huge head could be seen advancing over its surface. At first he seemed to take only a small bite out of it, but after a time it became evident that all of it was to disappear in his huge maw. It is not to be wondered at that, in terror, the natives flocked to Columbus and besought him to save their moon. They were confident that, since he knew of the coming of the monster—if indeed it was not by his behest that it had been sent—he would have the power to stay its progress, or else that he surely would be able to secure from the Great

Spirit some remission of this awful manifestation of His displeasure. For a certain well-
calculated length of time Columbus remained ob-
durate to their entreaties; but when he had
secured many promises from them, and when
the time of the eclipse was nearly elapsed, he
yielded to their prayers. Accordingly, though
the monster had swallowed the moon entire, they
now saw him visibly disgorge it, and soon their
beloved luminary was restored to them.

All who have heard this old story have, I am
sure, been deeply interested in it; but I wonder
how many of us have ever stopped to consider
that this definitely accurate knowledge on the
part of Columbus indicates a high state of astro-
nomic knowledge widely diffused at that period.
He must have been absolutely sure of his facts
about the matter, or he would not have dared to
put his credit with the Indians to the test of
prophecy. Navigators at the present time are, of
course, able to foretell such an astronomical incident, and would generally be in a position to
take advantage of it in their intercourse with
South Sea Islanders if it happened as oppor-
tunely as did this. Our modern navigators, however, have nautical almanacs provided for them
with great care and expense by scientific bureaus
under the orders of the various governments.
We are not likely to think that such books as
nautical almanacs were available in Columbus's
time. The fact of the matter is, nevertheless,
that sets of tables indicating the positions of the

heavenly bodies, and including the announcements of approaching eclipses, were published and widely circulated during the fifteenth century. One publication corresponding in many ways to our nautical almanacs was called a calendar; and the information it furnished was of the greatest service, at that time, to the bold navigators who did so much to spread geographical knowledge, and to make known, for succeeding generations, the surface of the earth.

Perhaps the most interesting detail of whatever information we possess with regard to these tables, at least so far as the modern world is concerned, is the fact that they were originally made and planned under the direction of an ecclesiastic living well up in the central portion of Europe, far from the seacoast,—a clergyman who was interested in astronomy and mathematics but scarcely at all in navigation. The usual impression is that at the period mentioned churchmen were discouraged from applying themselves to any form of science, and above all to astronomy. The Galileo case, a century and a half later, is supposed to be the proof of this; yet the tables which enabled Columbus to make the prophecy which so influenced the Indians were made by a man who was closely in touch with the Popes, and was invited down to Italy by them to correct the Calendar. Moreover, because of their respect for his astronomical knowledge, as well as his devotion to his clerical duties, the Pope made him Bishop of Ratisbon.

There is another story illustrative of the supposed astronomical knowledge of the middle of the fifteenth century, which, because of certain contrasting features, seems worth while placing in juxtaposition with this story of Columbus and the eclipse of the moon. In 1456, Halley's comet made a very striking appearance in the heavens, at one time extending over sixty degrees of the celestial vault. This was the first occasion on which any comet was observed with sufficient accuracy to supply data for calculating its path. Toscanelli's contemporary observations have been discussed in recent years, and are an evident proof of the care with which astronomical observations were made in his time, and of the extent of the knowledge possessed by professors of astronomy at Italian universities. Comets had always been considered harbingers of woe, and the unusual appearance of this one intensified the forebodings ordinarily produced by them.   It came, too, just at a moment when an overwhelming danger for Christendom seemed imminent. Constantinople had fallen into the hands of the Turks three years before, and it looked as though the Christian nations of Europe might all be subjected to the Sultan in the threatened wave of invasion which after the Moslem triumph in the East seemed inevitable.

At this time Calixtus III was Pope. His brief pontificate of scarcely three years was almost entirely occupied with a desperate but practically fruitless attempt to induce the Christian rulers of

Europe to lay aside their quarrels with one another and combine against this common foe.
When Halley's comet appeared, he is said to
have shared the terror of the people that this
might portend some awful calamity to Europe
from the Turks; and so, it is asserted, he issued
a Bull against the Turk and the comet. This
story has been accepted as one of the common-
places of history. From it men of all kinds
have drawn lessons as to the foolishness of the
ecclesiastics of the time; have denounced the in-
consistency of any claim for infallibility, with
such an exhibition of the extreme of human
tendency to error and superstition; and have declared the " Bull against the Comet " a fitting
illustration of what might be expected if men
submitted themselves to the dictates of the Pope.
It has been of no avail to point out that no such
Bull can be found in the collection of Papal
Bulls which are kept very faithfuly, and that the
general tenor of ecclesiastical thought with regard
to such astronomical phenomena makes it quite
absurd to suppose that any such Papal document
should have been issued.

Serious historians still continue to discuss the
subject, and every now and then some at least
supposedly educated person uses a reference to
the Papal Bull against the Turk and the comet
as a clinching innuendo against Papistry. Nothing in history is more amusing than the self-
complacent way in which each succeeding generation confidently assumes that its ancestors

have been absurdly foolish in their way of looking at things, and that we in our time are the
only ones in possession of real wisdom.   Of
course the whirligig of time brings in its re-
venges, and the great law of compensation will
be carried out when posterity pronounces a
similar judgment upon us.   In the meantime,
however, we shall continue to hear references to
this famous supposed Bull.

Those outside of the Church apparently know
much more about Papal Bulls that were never
issued than about those which were actual Papal
documents.   Here in America we are likely to
have the story of the Bull against the comet frequently recalled to us because of one of President Lincoln's expressions.   Not long after his
inauguration, he was urged by impatient Aboli-
tionists to put an end to slavery by proclama-
tion.   With the practical common-sense that
would have made his expression a great historical
phrase had his allusion only been true, he re-
plied that he was not disposed to issue a document which, in the state of affairs that existed
at that moment, would be as futile as the Pope's
Bull against the comet.

Now, this Bull against the comet is said to
have been issued by the immediate predecessor
of that Pope who a few years later summoned
Regiomontanus to Rome in order to correct the
Calendar, and rewarded him for his work in
science by making him Bishop of Ratisbon.   The
contrast of the two incidents should be enough

of itself, without any further discussion of the
question, to make it very clear that no such
Papal document had ever been issued, or else
that there had been a complete change of the
policy of the Popes in the course of a single
decade. As a matter of historical fact, we have
abundant evidence that distinguished churchmen
about this time were not only deeply interested,
in a thoroughly scientific way, in comets and
other astronomical subjects, but that they, especially, were the scholars who tried to do away
with the foolish fear harbored by many people,
even among the educated, that comets were
tokens of coming evil.

A typical example of this is to be found in
the works of St. Antoninus, Archbishop of Flor-
ence at the middle of the fifteenth century. In
his " Summa Historialis " he records that various
comets appeared about this time, and he discusses the nature and character of such bodies.
He considers that it is foolish to talk of them as
presaging evil, since they have a merely natural
origin. St. Antoninus was very close to the Popes
of this period, and there seems no doubt that
his expressions are the best evidence of the
general opinion held by ecclesiastics of his day
as to the nature of comets and their supposed influence upon man and terrestrial affairs. It is
true that St. Antoninus, following Albertus Magnus, supposed comets to be formed of earthly
vapors; but in this view he was merely express-
ing the universal consensus of the astronomers

of the age. A century later, in 1557, Tycho-
Brahé showed that comets were probably celestial bodies beyond our atmosphere; yet the teaching of Galileo and of Kepler, half a century after
Brahé's time, was closer to the view of St. Antoninus and Albertus Magnus than to that of
the great Danish astronomer, whose more correct theory did not meet a general acceptance for
nearly a century after his death, and two centuries after that of St. Antoninus.

Lest it should be thought that in this matter
we are tilting at an imaginary opponent, or that
the supposed issuance of the Bull against the
comet has not been accepted in recent years by
intelligent, educated men who ought to know
better, and who would never have accepted the
story so readily had they not been blinded by
their intolerant opposition to the Church, it seems
worth while quoting what Prof. John W. Draper,
in his *Conflict of Religion and Science,* had to
say in the matter. Prof. Draper's book was long
considered the last word on this subject. He
was supposed to have looked up his authorities
and to have consulted original documents, so
that there was no question about his facts. His
book was valued so highly by scientists that it
was thought worthy to be given a place in the
International Scientific Series, a collection that
everyone interested in the history and development of science was expected to have in his
library. Most of our public libraries put in the
complete set. This is how Prof. Draper, without

any warrant, disfigured and perverted the history
of science:

When Halley's comet came in 1456, so tremendous
was its apparition that it was necessary for the Pope
himself to interfere. He exorcised and expelled it
from the skies. It shrank away into the abysses of
space, terror stricken by the maledictions of Calixtus
III, and did not venture back for seventy-five years!
. . . By order of the Pope, all the church bells in
Europe were rung to scare it away; the faithful were
commanded to add each day another prayer; and as
their prayers had often in so marked a manner been
answered in eclipses and droughts and rains, so on this
occasion it was declared that the victory over the
comet had been vouchsafed to the Pope.

Prof. Andrew D. White went over this same
subject after Draper, and repeats the old story.
Pastor, the historian of the Popes, rightly dis-
misses it as absurd. There is no trace of the
Bull to be found though these documents as
fundamental ecclesiastical laws are preserved with
great care. The only evidence is a passing remark of a writer of the time the significance
of which has been exaggerated beyond all reason
and in a sense quite contrary to what we know
of the opinions of the scholars of the period by
those who were bent on making out a case against
the Popes.

In the light of these contrasting statements,
it will doubtless be of interest to those who
really want to know something concerning the
state of astronomical knowledge about the middle of the fifteenth century, and who care to

estimate by the easy method of biography the
fifteenth century attitude of the Church and of
ecclesiastics to astronomy, to read a brief sketch
of the life of the man to whom we owe the calendar, or almanac, to which Columbus was indebted
for his information with regard to the eclipse.
Regiomontanus, as he has come to be called, was
in private life John Miller,—or in German,
Johann Müller. In the Renaissance period, every
scholar was known by a Latin designation of
some kind,—usually the Latin name of his birth-
place. Regiomontanus having been born at
Königsberg (not the Königsberg in the north of
Germany, but that in Franconia, not far from
Munich), came to be called, after the fashion of
the time, Joannes de Monteregio, the Latin name
for Königsberg, or Royal Mountain. This did
not happen till a century after his death, when
his writings were printed,—that is, about the
middle of the sixteenth century (1542). Since
then he has been known in the history of science
by his literary designation, Regiomontanus.

Johann Müller was born in 1436, and died in
1476, when he was just past forty years of age,—
another striking proof that it is not the time-
element in work so much as the intensity-factor
that counts for accomplishment. During this
brief life span he had revolutionized the study
of astronomy, he had finished a work on trigo-
nometry in which he introduced the use of tan-
gents, had made all the calculations necessary
to reform the calendar, and had begun the pub-

lication of a series of astronomical observations
which were eminently helpful to all the students
of his age. These observations were continued
after his death; for, the initial difficulty being
surmounted, the continuation was easy. They
formed a precious incentive as well as a valuable
guide to the astronomers of the next century.
Yet all his life had not been devoted to astronomy: he had made his theological studies
with great success; he had been ordained a
clergyman; he had been especially successful in
his studies in Greek literature and language, and
had applied this knowledge to studying out what
the ancients had learned about science; and yet,
with all this he had been so faithful to his clerical
duties that he was selected as the Bishop of
Ratisbon.

Regiomontanus's career synchronized with a
period when, if we were to credit ordinary impressions and even the stories of classic historians, science scarcely existed at all. The reason for its non-existence is often loudly proclaimed to have been the opposition of the Church
authorities. There are, then, in his life two surprises,—supreme surprises. The first is that he
should have accomplished so much in physical
science and astronomy and mathematics about
the middle of the fifteenth century; the second
is that, having accomplished so much, and indeed having devoted himself more enthusiastically to this than to any other subject, far from
falling under the suspicion of the ecclesiastical

authorities, or being hindered in his work, or
discouraged in his publications, or hampered in
the enthusiastic movement which he was trying
to awaken for science, he was, on the contrary,
encouraged in every way, materially helped by
the ecclesiastical authorities, recommended to the
Popes as a man of deep scientific knowledge, invited to Rome to do his work there, and finally
raised to the hierarchy as a token not only of the
Pope's appreciation of the scientific work accomplished on the calendar, but of the honor
which the Church authorities thought due to his
scientific scholarship and his personal character.
The contrast is worth while emphasizing.

Young Müller was educated for the Church;
and his subsequent deep knowledge of Greek
seems to be evidence that the education afforded
to clerical students at this time was thorough and
broad.   His university studies were made in
Vienna, where he became the pupil of Purbach.
One would not be apt to think of Vienna in the
first half of the fifteenth century as possessing
a University in which could be secured good
courses in mathematics, and in at least certain of
the physical sciences, especially astronomy. Purbach, however, was doing some magnificent original work at the Vienna University, which had
been founded in the fourteenth century, and
which was still in the ardor of its first hundred
years of existence,— doing the work that every
university has done so well in its early days,
though all of them seem destined a little later

to degenerate into mere cultivators of routine knowledge,—places where groups of friends potter much over the things of the mind but accomplish very little except at intervals when genius wakes them up. Purbach and his pupil set themselves the huge task of testing the accuracy of the then accepted tables of the motions of the planets, which were those that had been published by Alphonso the Wise centuries before.

It is easy to understand that, with the extremely imperfect instruments which they possessed at the time—often, indeed, they had to construct their own—this must have seemed an almost impossible problem. The telescope was not invented until nearly two centuries later; yet these devoted students, in spite of their handicap, were able to accomplish much that was valuable. As a result of his deep interest in astronomy, Müller devoted himself to the study of Ptolemy's works. The fact that they were written in Greek made them difficult in those times. Constantinople had fallen only a few years before; and while the Greek scholars from that city who were wandering in Italy were beginning to create that furore which was to be the characteristic of the Renaissance, it is easy to understand that their influence had not penetrated as far as Vienna. The fact that Müller successfully learned Greek shows that, even before the fall of Constantinople, the European universities, or at least scholars in many parts of Europe, had been waking up to the beauties and the treasures contained in the Greek language and literature.

Purbach tried to secure the attention of as
many students as possible to astronomy; and it
is said to have been at his suggestion that young
Müller took up the work of providing an abridgment of Ptolemy's great work in a Latin translation, for those who might be deterred by the
Greek. It was only after Purbach's death, however, that the disciple was able to finish his translation and publish his Epitome of Ptolemy's
Almagest. This work had been very much
appreciated by the Arabs, to whom indeed we
owe its present name, *Almagest*. No better
treatise could have been selected for abridgment
with the purpose of reawakening the interest of
the generation in all that relates to astronomy.
This translation had one immediate good effect
for Müller: it attracted to him the attention of
Cardinal Bessarion, who was more interested in
Greek than in astronomy, and who desired above
all to spread the knowledge of the Greek language and literature among the Western nations.
The Cardinal became Müller's patron, and gave
the young astronomical student a much-desired
opportunity to study in Italy.

Müller chose Padua as the place where he
thought he could obtain the best facilities for the
further study of astronomy. It may seem
strange, perhaps, that this Italian University
should be thus chosen. It will doubtless be a
source of some surprise to those who have been
accustomed to think of Italian universities, all of
them directly under ecclesiastical control, as

surely preventing as far as possible the development of physical science. As a matter of fact, however, physical science of all kinds as well as scholarship of all kinds, was being cultivated most assiduously in every Italian university of the time. Padua and Bologna both provided excellent opportunities in anatomy and all the sciences relating to medicine; and the names of the men who were there at work in science are well known to the modern generation. Whenever a serious student in any part of Europe wanted to get fuller opportunities for post-graduate work, he went to Italy. Before the end of the century a number of Englishmen, among them Bishop Selling, John Phreas, and Linacre, took advantage of the facilities of Italian education, and spent years in the Italian universities.

What Germany was during the latter half of the nineteenth century in post-graduate work, Italy was for some six centuries before the nineteenth. Where ecclesiastical influence was the greatest, there the ardor for study was the highest, and the facilities for education the best. This is as true of the physical sciences as of Latin and Greek. At the beginning of the sixteenth century, Vesalius went down to Italy for wider opportunities for study in anatomy; just as Steno, the great Danish anatomist, did at the beginning of the next century. Some twenty-five years after Müller went to Padua for astronomy, Copernicus also made the journey to that

University, and studied the same science under
Novara. He studied medicine also, and took his
degree at that greatest existing teaching institution of the world. All this is so different from
ordinary impressions about the matter that it
deserves to be particularly dwelt on.

After his Italian experience, lasting nearly ten
years Müller returned to Germany to take up his
life-work. He was then about thirty-five years
of age. His astronomical knowledge brought
him into contact with Bernard Walther, a
wealthy merchant of Nuremberg, and at the same
time an enthusiastic astronomer. Walther belonged to one of the town's old patrician families,
all of whom prided themselves on having deep
intellectual as well as mercantile interests. The
town itself was one of the chief commercial cen-
tres of the world, and yet was known for its
devotion to the things of the mind. It was
famous not only as a home of marvellous German, industry, manufactures, and ingenious inventions—a reputation which it has maintained
down to the present day—but also as a seat of
culture and education. Those who know their
Renaissance well will recall the Pirkheimer
family of Nuremberg; and the story of the wide
culture and profound intellectual interests of
Willibald and Charity Pirkheimer is itself abundant evidence of the town's prominence in the intellectual life of Europe during the century from
1450 to 1550.

In connexion with Bernard Walther, then,

Müller began the erection of an observatory. In many ways this structure at Nuremberg was ideally situated, though one must recall conditions in the old south German town to realize this. The place was, and has always been, famous for its locksmiths, its workers in iron and in metal of all kinds, and for the ingenuity and inventiveness of its artisans. Walther's wealth enabled him to secure the finest instruments that could be obtained at the time. The most skilful artisans of Nuremberg were commissioned to employ all their inventive genius to put instrumental aids at the command of the observers. As a consequence, some of the first ingenious mechanical appliances for astronomical observatories were made and used here. Clocks driven by weights, for instance, were here employed for the first time for scientific purposes. The observatory became quite a show-place for astronomical students, because of the ingenious inventions it contained. Descriptions of these promptly led to their imitation, and improved very much the mechanical side of astronomical observatories throughout Europe.

The observatory, however, soon became famous for other reasons than its ingenious equipment. Good scientific work, which attracted widespread attention, was reported therefrom. The work done by Müller and Walther almost invariably had a practical side, which made it of great value at that period. Probably the most notable improvement introduced into practical astronomy was the substitution of Venus for the moon, as a connecting link between observations of the sun and of the stars. Venus has continued practically down to our own day to occupy the prominent place thus given her by Müller; and the transits of Venus—that is, the passage of that planet across the disk of the sun—have been taken advantage of in order to correct our knowledge of the distance of the sun from the earth. Another important practical discovery made by Müller was the influence of refraction in altering the apparent places of the stars.

It was because of his publications, however, that Müller (or Regiomontanus, as I suppose he should be called in connexion with these, for it is to them he owes the Latin form of his name) attracted the attention of not only astronomical students and observers, but also navigators, geographers, and practically all those interested in physical science, not to say the educated classes generally. He seems to have appreciated the value of publicity as an incentive to scientific work. The making of observations might be an intense pleasure for the observer; but if these were to be useful to other students and to mankind, they must be published, though publication involved an immense amount of trouble. Regiomontanus was tireless in bringing out calendars and ephemerides. Contrary to the customs of the time, these were not printed exclusively in Latin, but there were also popular editions in German; and these are probably the first scientific works

ever published in the German vernacular. His
first calendar, known as " Magister Johann von
Kunsperk's teutscher Kalendar " (sic), was published about 1473. The curious abbreviation of
Königsberg into the colloquial Kunsperk is noteworthy; as also the absence of the capital and
the use of the *t* instead of the *d* in the word
" teutsch."

A number of these calendars, in the various
vernaculars, were issued during the fourteenth
and fifteenth centuries. Probably the best idea
of how frequent was their issue can be gathered
from the following list of calendars in English
that are to be found among the manuscripts of
the British Museum. Father John Gerard, S. J.,
who gives the list, says that " this is not all, but
only some, of the calendars of that time." The
English, of course were mariners, and there was
a distinct demand for such information as was
thus provided; but it is probable that Spain and
Portugal and Italy had even more of them.
These mentioned, however, will serve to show
how contrary to reality is any assertion as to
lack of knowledge or interest in astronomical
information during the later Middle Ages. There
are: " A Calendar drawn up in 1327, with pre-
diction of eclipses, solar, and lunar, to 1386
(Sloane, 286). An Almanack, with eclipses of
the sun, 1380-1462, calculated for the meridian
of Oxford: composed for Johanna, mother of
Richard II., by John Somar, a Franciscan (Sloane,
282); An Almanack, with eclipses, 1387-1462

(Arundel, 207) ; an Almanack, including eclipses
of the sun from 1431 to 1462 (Additional, 17,-
358) ; Almanack for 1431, with eclipses to 1462,
and a suitable tract concerning the rules for their
computation: this is arranged to hang for reference at the girdle (Harley, 937). Tested by
modern tables, the forecasts were quite correct.

The Latin editions of Müller's work were
called *Kalendarium Novum*. There were numerous editions, and translations were made into
German and Italian. Besides these more popular publications, Regiomontanus issued the
Ephemerides Astronomicæ, also in Latin. The
publication of these began in 1473; and, as the
result of the interest manifested in them during
the author's life, they continued to be issued by
Walther until the latter's death in 1504. The
material accumulated served for further issues
until 1506. These publications were widely read
in popular as well as scientific circles. The well-
known navigator and cartographer, Martin
Behem (or Behaim), who, born at Nuremberg
in the same year as Müller, was naturally much
interested in his fellow-townsman's work, and
spread the knowledge of it abroad, especially
among Spanish and Portuguese navigators.
Behem became in 1484 geographer to the expedition of Diego Cam, which went to the western coast of Africa, and did much for fifteenth-
century geographical science. How highly his
services were appreciated, and how much reward
they were thought to deserve, may be judged

from the fact that, when Behem returned from Lisbon, the dignity of knighthood was conferred upon him, and he was employed by the King in many honorable positions.

It is through Behem, as has been said, that Regiomontanus's publications became well known to the Spanish and Portuguese navigators. His influence on Columbus, Bartholomew Diaz, and Vasco da Gama can readily be understood. After 1486, Behem lived for many years at Fayal in the Azores, where he had married the daughter of Huerter, the governor of the Flemish colony on those islands. He visited Nuremberg in 1493; and while there, in order to illustrate to his townsmen the present state of geography as the Spaniards and Portuguese had been making it, he constructed a terrestrial globe. This globe is still preserved, and has been frequently reproduced. Constructed before Columbus' discovery, it is easy to understand that the instrument shows many errors; but it is a striking testimony to the general excellence of geographic knowledge at this time, and above all to the fact that such knowledge had reached a stage far beyond what the average modern is likely to imagine. It is easy to understand, too, how the man who made this globe would have influenced the Spanish and Portuguese navigators of the period, and so we are able to trace the direct connecting link between him and such men as Columbus and Vasco da Gama.

The reputation of the Nuremberg astronomer

now recommended him to Pope Sixtus IV as
the best man to assist in reforming the Calendar.
The Pontiff accordingly summoned him to Rome.
This was probably in the early part of 1476.
Unfortunately, the great astronomer contracted
Roman fever and died July 6 of the same year.
As is so often the way .with foreigners, the
fever ran a very rapid course and death came
speedily. In his case, as in nearly all instances
of unlooked-for death occurring in the Middle
Ages, there has been a suggestion of poison; but
there is absolutely no reason for such a suspicion,
as Regiomontanus had no enemies and many
friends. People may die rapidly for ever so
many reasons of which we find no trace in the
history of the Middle Ages. All the cases of
appendicitis, for example, which so often run a
course resembling poisoning, since there is sudden
pain and then peritonitis and collapse, with a
pouring-out of offensive material into the abdomen, as though some corrosive poison had bored
a hole in the intestines, are unaccounted for,
unless we take some of these so-called poisoning
cases to represent them.   There are sudden
deaths of many other kinds,—from heart disease,
from fulminant pneumonia, fulminant malaria
(as in this case), and the malignant types of the
infectious diseases, which might well be taken
for poisoning cases among a people ignorant of
modern advances in medical diagnosis. We know
very well the poisons that they had in the Middle
Ages, and none of them is of the insidious char-

acter which is such a commonplace in history.
Regiomontanus suffered, as did many another
foreigner, from injudicious exposure, and nothing more. The fact that, somehow, the usual
suspicion of poisoning is attached to his death is
only another evidence of how much judicious
criticism, in the light of modern medical discovery, must be exercised with regard to these
reported Middle-Age poisonings, which are considered to have blackened the character of so
many prominent historical personages.

It was during the months spent in Rome that
Müller commended himself so much to the Pope
for his piety and his scholarship that he was
selected as the Bishop of Ratisbon. Just about
two centuries before, another great teacher and
investigator in physical science, Albertus Magnus, had been made bishop of this same see.
The three centuries from the birth of the first
of these two men to the death of the second,
represent the time when the Church was supremely dominant in European education. It is
illuminating, then, to find that in the thirteenth
and fifteenth centuries scientific scholarship of
the profoundest kind, with devotion to scientific
investigation that has never been surpassed, was
not only no bar to ecclesiastical preferment, but
was evidently even an added reason why the respective Popes of those periods selected these
two great Bishops of the See of Ratisbon. Nothing that I know of is a more complete answer
to the assertions of historians who insist on

Church opposition to science during the Middle
Ages, than this conjunction of Albertus Magnus
and Regiomontanus as brother bishops of the
same see, with two centuries of interval.

It may possibly seem to many people that the
scientific devotion which characterized Regiomontanus's work is due to the Renaissance, and
therefore to a spirit quite foreign to that which
ruled the Middle Ages. It may even be suspected, at least, that that spirit of inquiry which
is supposed to have awakened during the latter
part of the fifteenth century, and to have eventually led up to the Reformation in the sixteenth,
was already abroad, and because of this it was
that Regiomontanus did his wonderful work in
science. Some may indeed suggest that perhaps
it was well that Regiomontanus died when he
did; for had he lived, his scientific speculations
would, in the opinion of these objectors, have
almost surely brought him into trouble with the
ecclesiastical authorities. Men who talk in this
way can know nothing of the life of Regiomontanus's great predecessor in the See of Ratisbon
two centuries before. A brief résumé of the
knowledge of Albertus Magnus in the geographical and astronomical subjects for which
his eminent successor was to do so much, will
show very clearly that the latter is a legitimate
descendant of the intellectual spirit of the former.

In the sketch of Albert's life which precedes
this, I have quoted a paragraph from Albert's
biographer, Sighart, in which all the ideas with

regard to the earth, that are supposed to be ever so much more modern than the thirteenth century, are mentioned as contained in Albert's work. Not only that, but all the teachings of geography and science that are supposed to have been so bitterly opposed by the Church, because they contained apparent contradictions of the Scriptures, are here anticipated in the works of a man who was in the closest union with the ecclesiastical authorities of his time. Albertus Magnus was looked up to by his own and succeeding generations as a saint; he has been declared Blessed, and doubtless will later be raised to the altar; yet his writings with regard to astronomy and geography are just such as are usually said, by those who know no better, to have been the special execration of the ecclesiastics of his time. With this paragraph in view, it is easy to understand the sympathetic appreciation of Regiomontanus two centuries later.

To sum up, then, the career of Regiomontanus furnishes some interesting reflections on the ordinary impressions that are so often accepted, even by the educated, with regard to his period and the body of men to which he belonged. We find that in the fifteenth century astronomy was a subject of vivid interest, and that new information with regard to it was rapidly diffused throughout Europe. We find that ecclesiastics, far from being opposed to the development of the science, were the pioneer workers in it,—the men of leisure who had the chance, and took it, to develop science out of as yet unorganized knowledge. We find, moreover, that ecclesiastical preferment awaited those who were successful in scientific research, provided their other qualities justified it; and that clergymen in high places were the progressive thinkers, even in physical science. Above all, the fact that Regiomontanus should have been Albertus Magnus's successor as Bishop of Ratisbon emphasizes the truth that the policy of the Church had not changed during the two centuries that separate these men, and that their lives must be the criteria by which we may best judge of the attitude of the Church to science during the wonderful later Middle Ages, before either the Renaissance or the Reformation (so-called) came to disturb the intellectual life of Europe.

VI.

CLERICAL PIONEERS IN ELECTRICITY.

Causa latet, vis est notissima.—Ovid.

WHEN I consider the multitude of associate forces which are diffused through nature—when I think of that calm and tranquil balancing of their energies which enables elements most powerful in themselves, most destructive to the world's creatures and economy, to dwell associated together and be made subservient to the wants of creation, I rise from the contemplation more than ever impressed with the wisdom, the beneficence, and grandeur beyond our language to express, of the Great Disposer of all.—Faraday.

THE man of science must look upon his pursuits, if he understands them rightly, as an exercise of Religion.—Oersted.

A life spent in the contemplation of the productions of divine power, wisdom, and goodness, would be a life of devotion.—Priestley.

ABBÉ NOLLET

CLERICAL PIONEERS IN ELECTRICITY.

ELECTRICAL and magnetic phenomena are so surprising in themselves, so seductive in their mystery, and therefore so likely to attract the attention of the intelligent observer, that it might almost confidently be expected that clergymen with some leisure on their hands, who were at all interested in natural science, or what we would now call nature study, would quite naturally, in the days when little was known about electrical science, devote some time at least to the investigation of it. The fact that the names of very few clergymen are known in this connexion would seem to indicate that at the time when only the curious things about the as yet unborn science of electricity—the phenomena of magnetic attraction and repulsion and of electrical manifestations after the rubbing of various substances—were known, clergymen had but very little of intellectual curiosity or zest for observation and experiment, or else were prevented from investigation of these curious phenomena, either by direct prohibition of such studies to churchmen or else by the feeling that such studies might be dangerous to their faith. The supposition, however, that clergymen did not investigate these very surprising manifestations, I have recently found while reading up some of the early history of electricity, is entirely gratuitous and unfounded.

Not long since I had occasion to go over Priestley's *History of Electricity,* published originally just after the middle of the eighteenth century, and it is little short of marvelous to find how many Catholic clergymen had made important observations on electrical and magnetic phenomena during the first half of this century, and thus helped to bring a new science into that vogue which it already enjoyed when Franklin's work began. A brief list of these and their principal discoveries will make clear what an interesting chapter in the history of science is here opened up. Father Beccaria in Italy investigated the relations of electricity to air and water. Abbé Nollet in France made observations on the effects of electricity on animals and plants. Abbé Menon also in France made additional observations on the effects of electricity on animals. Canon Von Kleist of Kammin, in North Germany, invented the Leyden jar. Professor Gordon, a Scotch Benedictine monk, invented the first practical frictional electrical machine. Besides these there was Father Prenditz in Bohemia, a Premonstratensian monk, who suggested the identity of lightning and electricity, apparently quite independently of Franklin, and almost at the same time. Then, before the end of the century, there was Abbé Haüy, the father of crystallography, who studied pyro-electricity successfully, and invented a method of preventing the compass from being improperly affected by iron or steel in its immediate neighborhood, which was of the greatest possible service to mariners, and is indeed the basis of such precautionary provisions that are so necessary in our iron, or rather steel, vessels of the modern time.

It has occurred to me that an account of the discoveries made by these men, with brief sketches of their careers as far as they are available, would be of interest to clergymen generally, for the science of electricity has always maintained its attractiveness for the Catholic clergy. Besides, the materials thus gathered will furnish additional and quite convincing evidence of the fact that there is not and never was any opposition between science and reilgion, and that it is quite possible for a man to accept all the principles of religion on faith and yet retain a mind perfectly open to all the possible suggestions of experimental science, absolutely free to follow all the avenues of investigation that may suggest themselves, quite untrammeled to accept such conclusions as may be reached by the experimental method. Indeed it is from the history of clerical contributions to science that this absolutely false notion is best controverted and shown to be the result of an intolerant assumption on the part of those who protest so much against ecclesiastical intolerance with regard to science.

It will be found that all of these clergymen who devoted themselves so successfully to the study of electrical phenomena were distinguished for their inquiring disposition, their scientific temperament and painstaking devotion to the experimental method, so that they were not likely to miss the significance of their observations. Authority might mean much to them in the realm of religion, but they knew no trammels in the field of science, and sought truth as the result of questions put to nature quite as strenuously as the veriest of sceptics in matters of faith.

It is sometimes thought that electricity or, to be more accurate, the phenomena of magnetism which were known to the older generations attracted very little attention until comparatively recent times. Franklin's excursion into the subject here in America is supposed to have attracted the world-wide atention that it did mainly because it was such distinctly original and unusual work. It was as if people had not thought of the possibility of the development of a science of electricity before his epoch-making observations and investigations. While not wishing to diminish by jot or tittle Franklin's well-deserved glory in science, such an impression is completely erroneous. Men were interested in the phenomena of magnetism particularly and in certain electrical manifestations from very early times.

The inquiring geniuses who made the thirteenth century what it was in the history of education had an all-pervading curiosity, which would not allow so interesting a subject as magnetism and its possibilities to escape them.

Brother Potamian summed up not long since in the introduction to a translation of the famous letter of Petrus Peregrinus on magnetic phenomena, which was written in the thirteenth century, a large number of references to magnetism which occur in the literature of the thirteenth century. A single paragraph from this will serve to show how widespread was the interest and how much men were occupied with natural phenomena at a time when the study of nature, according to most of our modern histories of education, is supposed to have been very far from men's thoughts. Brother Potamian says:

Abbot Neckam, the Augustinian (1157-1215), distinguishes between the properties of the two ends of the lodestone, and gives in his *De Utensilibus* what is, perhaps, the earliest reference to the Mariner's compass that we have. Albertus Magnus, the Dominican (1193-1280), in his treatise *De Mineralibus*, enumerates different kinds of natural magnets and states some of the properties commonly attributed to them. The minstrel Guyot de Provins, in a famous satirical poem, written about 1208, refers to the directive quality of the lodestone and its use in navigation; as do also Cardinal de Vitry, in his *Historia Orientalis* (1215-1220) ; Brunetto Latini, poet, orator and philosopher, in his *Trésor des Sciences*, a veritable library, written in Paris in 1260; Raymond Lully, the Enlightened Doctor, in his treatise *De Contemplatione*, begun in 1272, and Guido Guinicelli, the poet-priest of Bologna, who died in 1276.[1]

[1] The Letter of Petrus Peregrinus on the Magnet (A. D. 1269), translated by Brother Arnold, M.Sc., Principal of La Salle Institute, Troy, with Introductory Notice by Brother Potamian, Professor of Physics in Manhattan College, N. Y. McGraw, N. Y., 1902.

Guyot de Provins was a famous trouvère of the thirteenth century, but like most of the poets of this time had many hints of the knowledge that was beginning to accumulate in the University world of his time. Indeed it is from the writings of men such as he that we know how much of scientific information there was abroad at this time. Dante, for instance, knew more of the science of his time than any modern poet does of science, and some of the scientific information that he used merely as figures shows a marvelous anticipation of modern knowledge. Guyot describes the compass and shows that he knew about its use and its usefulness. Like more than one of the distinguished poets of the time, when he passed middle life Guyot turned to the Cloister as a refuge and a solace, and entered a Benedictine abbey where he died as one of the members of the great Order that had done so much to preserve and develop learning during the centuries when the transition period from barbarism to modern civilization was working itself out among the people who had taken the place of the Romans in the history of the world.

It is evident that most of those who were interested in magnetic phenomena about the time of the beginning of the universities were clergymen. Only one of those mentioned by Brother Potamian was not an ecclesiastic. There seems to have been one of these special periods of interest in a definite department of science in the thirteenth century with regard to magnetism.

One of the great practical results of this was the perfection of the mariner's compass. After this century, however, neglect came over this department of magnetism until Gilbert's time. He was a contemporary of Francis Bacon, and did so much for the science of electricity that it was never quite to sink out of sight again. The great revival of interest in the subject came, however, at the beginning of the eighteenth century, and then, as in the thirteenth century, the most important contributors to it were once more ecclesiastics.

As in every other form of science at this time, the Jesuits were leaders. For half a century their men had been doing some of the best work in astronomy in the world of science at that time. It is easy to understand that magnetism attracted their attention, and that some of them succeeded in making original observations of great value. Two of them deserve to be mentioned here. Father Cabeo, an Italian Jesuit, wrote a treatise that was really intended as a text-book on Magnetism, called *Philosophiae Ars Magnetica*, which was published at Ferrara in 1629. He had made a series of observations on the magnet and its curious effects, and above all he had noted how iron-filings arranged themselves in particular lines which evidently represent the lines of force of magnetic attraction. He has not only described these phenomena, but has made also an excellent picture of it, the first in literature, which is to be found in this text-book of his.

The other Jesuit who deserves to be mentioned
at this time is Father Strada whose *Prolusiones
Academicae* (Lyons, 1617) contains a poem
treating particularly of magnetic and electric phenomena. Perhaps the most wonderful passage
in this is that in which Father Strada tells a
story that he had heard of two clergymen who
had learned to communicate with one another at
a distance. According to this account the friends
had what we would call a sympathetic or magnetic telegraph consisting of dials on which the
letters of the alphabet were printed. A mag-
netized pointer swung freely above these letters,
and whenever one of the pointers was turned by
hand to a particular letter, the other by sympathy
or magnetic attraction even at a distance turned
to the same letter. In this way the friends were
able to communicate with one onother. The
story of course is a wonderful anticipation of
wireless telegraphy, and shows how far the
human imagination can outstrip the human intellect in reaching conclusions. This is probably
the first hint of wireless telegraphy that ever
was made. A century and a-half later, however,
and more than a century before wireless telegraphy became an accomplished fact, two clergymen are said to have communicated with one
another between Spain and the Madeira Islands
by means of electric signals conveyed through
the water. How much truth there may be in this
second story it is hard to determine, but at least
the story is over a hundred years old.

When Franklin appeared on the scene with his interest in electricity, about the middle of the eighteenth century, far from opening up a new subject then or even one in which his particular generation had not been interested, as is so often thought, he had really taken up a branch of science that had attracted no little attention from the men of immediately preceding generations. Anyone who wishes to realize this should consult the *History and Present State of Electricity, with Original Experiments,* written by the famous English scientist Joseph Priestley to whom we owe the discovery of oxygen and most of our knowledge with regard to oxidation processes. The original edition of this *History of Electricity,*[2] which is in two volumes and contains altogether nearly one thousand pages, probably over 250,000 words was issued in 1757. It will be remembered that Franklin's kite experiments were made about 1750 and that his work in electricity attracted attention in Europe during this sixth decade of the eighteenth century. How lively was the interest in the subject of electricity can be best appreciated very probably from the fact that a second edition of Priestley's

[2] The History and Present State of Electricity, with Original Experiments, by Joseph Priestley, LL.D., F.R.S. The Third edition corrected and enlarged. London, Printed for C. Bathhurst, and T. Lowndes, in Fleet-Street; J. Rivington and J. Johnson, in St. Paul's Churchyard; S. Crowder, G. Robinson, and R. Baldwin, in Paternoster Row; T. Becket, and T. Cadell, in the Strand. MDCCLXXV.

History was called for within three years, and
that a third was issued in 1775. This history indeed gave him almost more of the reputation as
a scientist which he enjoyed when he came to
this country than did his original work in
chemistry.

The most distinguished of these clergymen
pioneers in electricity was undoubtedly Giovanni
Battista Beccaria, who was distinguished not
only for his work in electricity, but also for his
devotion to practical astronomy, and his contributions to the physical sciences in matters related to both these subjects. He was born at
Mondovi, a small town situated in the Province
of Cuneo in Northern Italy and not far from the
French border. A battle was fought in this
neighborhood, some 80 years after his birth
which makes the name of the town more familiar
than it otherwise would be. Beccaria was born
7 October, 1716, and at the early age of sixteen
entered the religious order of the Fathers of the
Pious Schools. He was looked upon as a very
promising student, and was given special opportunities to devote himself to favorite branches.
Curious as it may seem to those who think of
the teaching of science as a comparatively
modern introduction into schools, and especially
Catholic schools, Beccaria received special training to become a professor of experimental
physics.

He was given a professorship in this, in connexion with his own order, first at Palermo in

Sicily and later at Rome. At the early age of twenty-two he was transferred to a similar position, but of more importance from an educational standpoint, at Turin. While here he was asked to become the tutor to the young princes of Chablais and de Carignan. As a consequence of this official position, though it was the custom of his order to transfer teachers from one school to another after intervals cf a few years, Beccaria was not moved from Turin for many years and it eventually came to be his place of residence for most of the remainder of his life.

That his scientific work soon began to attract world-wide attention will perhaps best be appreciated from the fact that in May, 1775, when he was not yet forty years of age, he was elected a Fellow of the Royal Society of London. This was a much envied distinction at the time and one not usually conferred on any except those who had done distinctly original work of a high order in science. As a consequence of his election Father Beccaria communicated several important papers relating to his investigation into electricity and various astronomical subjects directly to the Royal Society and these gave him a further reputation among English-speaking people.

No great discovery in physical science is attached to his name, but few men did as much as he to awaken enthusiasm for experimental investigation into science in his time. He was thus a very active factor in bringing about the marvelous burst of progress in the physical sciences generally, which came at the end of the eighteenth and the beginning of the nineteenth century. It is this which so successfully ushered in the modern scientific era of which we are so proud.

The value of his observations have been universally acknowledged. It is not too much to say that what he accomplished with regard to the relation of electricity to meteorological phenomena practically laid the foundation of a new science of meteorology. In his masterly article on electricity in the eighth volume of the ninth edition of the *Encyclopedia Britannica,* which is often referred to as a compendious authoritative review of the development of this science, Prof. George Chrystal, the Professor of Mathematics at the University of St. Andrews, Edinburgh, has summed up Father Beccaria's contributions to electricity and meteorology. The thoroughly conservative character of Prof. Chrystal's judgment makes it clear how distinguished is the place Father Beccaria must be considered to hold in the history of these sciences:

Beccaria, a celebrated Italian physicist, kept up the spirit of electrical discovery in Italy. He showed that water is a very imperfect conductor of electricity, that its conducting power is proportional to its quantity, and that a small quantity of water opposes a powerful resistance to the passage of electricity. He succeeded in making the electric spark visible in water by discharging shocks through wires that nearly met in tubes filled with water. In this experiment the tubes, though sometimes eight or ten lines thick, were burst into pieces. Beccaria likewise demonstrated that air adjacent to an electrified body gradually acquired the same electricity; that the electricity of the body is diminished by that of air; and that the air parts with its electricity very slowly. He considered that there was a mutual repulsion between the particles of the electric fluid and those of air, and that in the passage of the former through the latter a temporary vacuum was formed. Beccaria's experiments on atmospherical electricity are of the greatest interest to the meteorologist.

In his *History of Electricity* already mentioned, the first edition of which it may be recalled was issued two years after Father Beccaria's election as a Fellow of the Royal Society of London, Priestley, who always calls him Signior Beccaria, says that he was one of the most eminent of all the electricians on the Continent. He describes some of Father Beccaria's experiments on air and its relations to electricity, and calls attention to the fact that he had arranged his experiments .or this matter very ingeniously or, as Priestley puts it, " in a pleasing and satisfactory manner." Priestley was so taken with the experiments arranged by the Italian clerical observer that he gives them in considerable detail. Because his description serves to bring out the thoroughly experimental character of the work at a time when habits of experiment are supposed to have been uncommon and most of all among clergymen, it has seemed worth while to reproduce here what Priestley says:

Beccaria proves that the air, which is contiguous to

an electrified body, acquires by degrees the same electricity; that this electricity of the air counteracts that of
the body, and lessens its effects, and that as the air acquires, so it also parts with this electricity very slowly.

He began his experiments by hanging his linen
threads upon an electrified chain and observing that
they diverged the most after a few turns of his globe.
After that they came nearer together, notwithstanding
he kept turning the globe and the excitation was as
powerful as ever.

When he had kept the chain electrified a considerable
time, and then discontinued the friction, the threads
collapsed by degrees, till they hung parallel, and then
began to diverge again as before. Thus the second divergence of the threads took place, when the chain was
deprived of its electricity, and when that which the air
had acquired began to show itself.

While the threads were beginning to diverge with the
electricity of the air, if he touched the chain, and
thereby took off what remained of its electricity, the
threads would separate farther. Thus the more the
electricity of the chain was lessened, the more did the
electricity of the air appear.

While the threads were in their second divergence he
hung two other threads shorter than the former by another silk thread to the chain; and when all the electricity of the chain was taken quite away, they would
separate like the former threads.

If he presented other threads to the former, in their
second divergence, they would all avoid one another.

In this complete and elegant manner did Signior
Beccaria demonstrate that air actually receives electricity by communication, and loses it by degrees; and
then the electricity of the air counteracts that of the
body which conveys electricity to it.

Signior Beccaria also made a variety of other experiments which demonstrate other mutual affections of
the air and the electric fluid, particularly some that
prove their mutual repulsion, and that the electric fluid

in passing through any portion of air makes a temporary vacuum.

He brought the ends of two wires within a small distance of one another, in a glass tube, one end of which was closed and the other immerged in water, and observed that the water sank in the tube every time that a spark passed from the one to the other, the electric fluid having repelled the air.

Some further variations in his methods of experiment show at once Father Beccaria's ingenuity of mind and also how persistent he was in putting questions to nature. This is perhaps even better illustrated in Father Beccaria's experiments on water than in those with regard to air. Priestley has once more expressed his admiration for the work done in this line and has given an excellent résumé of what the Italian clergyman-scientist succeeded in discovering. His account is so compressed, yet so clear, it represents so well the significance of Father Beccaria's experiments as seen from the standpoint of a contemporary, and makes so clear the interest which all this experimental science was arousing all over Europe, that I venture to make another rather lengthy quotation from Priestley:

Signior Beccaria's experiments on the water, showing its imperfections as a conductor, are more surprising than those he made upon air, showing its imperfections in the contrary respect. They prove that water conducts electricity according to its quantity, and that a small quantity of water makes a very great resistance to the passage of the electric fluid.

He made tubes full of water part of the electric

circuit, and observed that when they were very small they would not transmit a shock, but that the shock increased as wider tubes were used.

But what astonishes us most in Signior Beccaria's experiments with water is his making the electric spark visible in it, notwithstanding its being a real conductor of electricity. Nothing, however, can prove more clearly how imperfect a conductor it is.

He inserted wires, so far as nearly to meet, in small tubes filled with water, and, discharging shocks through them, the electric spark was visible between their points as if no water had been in the place. The tubes were generally broken to pieces, and the fragments driven to a considerable distance. This was evidently occasioned by the repulsion of the water and its compressibility, it not being able to give way far enough within itself, and the force with which it was repelled being very great.

The force with which small quantities of water are thus repelled by the electric fluid, he says, is prodigious. By means of a charge of four hundred square inches he broke a glass tube two lines thick, when the pieces were driven to the distance of twenty feet. Nay, he sometimes broke tubes eight or ten lines thick, and fragments were driven to greater distances in proportion.

He found the effect of the electric spark upon water greater than the effect of a spark of common fire on gunpowder; and he says he does not doubt but that, if a method could be found of managing them equally well, a cannon charged with water would be more dreadful than one charged with gunpowder. He actually charged a glass tube with water, and put a small ball into it, when it was discharged with great force, so as to bury itself in some clay which he had placed to receive it.

After Father Beccaria, the most distinguished experimental scientist in electrical matters during the first half of the eighteenth century was the Abbé Nollet, who is famous for his series of experiments on the effects of electricity on animals and plants at this time. Priestley concedes the priority in this field of investigation to Abbé Nollet, and says that the English philosophers who led the way in almost every other application of electricity were among the last to try its effects upon animals and other organized bodies. Nollet began his experiments in this department by studying first the evaporation of fluids by electricity. The conclusions which he reached from his experiments are quoted in full in his own words in Priestley, and give the best possible idea of how patient must have been his investigation, how ingenious his methods of experimentation, and how carefully his observations were controlled before he ventured to give them forth as having scientific value.

Electricity augments the natural evaporation of fluids; since, excepting mercury, which is too heavy, and the oil of olives, which is too viscous, all the others which are tried suffered a diminution which could not be ascribed to any other cause than electricity.

Electricity augments the evaporation of those fluids the most which are most subject to evaporate of themselves. For the volatile spirit of sal ammoniac suffered a greater loss than spirit of wine or turpentine; these two more than common water, and water more than vinegar or the solution of nitre.

Electricity has a greater effect upon fluids when the vessels which contain them are non-electrics, the effects always seeming to be a little greater when the vessels were of metal than when they were of glass.

This increased evaporation was more considerable

when the vessel which contained the ·liquor was more open, but the effects did not increase in proportion to their apertures. For when these liquors were electrified in vessels whose aperture was four inches in diameter, though they presented to the air a surface sixteen times larger than when they were contained in vessels whose aperture was one inch in diameter, they were, nevertheless, far from suffering a diminution proportioned to that difference.

Electrification does not make any liquors evaporate through the pores, either of metal or of glass, since after experiments which were continued ten hours there was found no diminution of their weight when the vessels in which they were contained were well stopped.

Abbé Nollet's years ran almost coincident with the eighteenth century. He was born at Pimprez in what is now the district of Oise, in 1700, and, like many another distinguished observer in physical science, lived to fill out seventy years of studious life. He was born of poor parents, and owed his opportunity to receive an education to the fact that his parish priest became interested in him, and that he was educated at the expense of the Church. How much his contemporaries, even in foreign countries, thought of him can be judged from his election to the Royal Society of London in 1734, when he was not yet thirty-five years of age. Just before his fiftieth birthday he became a member of the Academy of Sciences of Paris. These distinctions were for work done in electricity before Franklin took up the subject. It is not surprising, then, that the genial Abbé was appointed to a newly-erected chair of experimental physics, in the college of Navarre in Paris, in 1753. He was undoubtedly one of the most popular writers on science during the century. He did more than perhaps any other to make the general public realize how much was being done, all over the world, for the progress of electricity, and to give them an interest in various phases of electrical science. In the historical Introduction to his article on electricity in the *Encyclopedia Britannica*, Professor Chrystal of Saint Andrews, whom we have already quoted with regard to Father Beccaria, gives Abbé Nollet a merited place among the investigators of electricity just before and after Franklin's time. Those who think that Franklin's writings were pioneer publications in this field will probably be not a little surprised here to learn that Nollet's *Essai sur l'Electricité* was published in 1746, and that his *Récherches,* containing many additional articles on the same subject, was published in 1749. The year 1750 is sometimes said to be a landmark which represents the beginning of modern electricity, but this is only true if we neglect a series of important communications made before that, and indeed Franklin's work, as we have already said, was only a manifestation in America of an enthusiasm for electrical studies which had been awakened in every country in Europe toward the end of the first half of the eighteenth century.

It was not alone on full-grown and highly-

organized living things that Abbé Nollet made
his experiments, but also on seeds and plants in
the process of growth.   These experiments have
been confirmed by many later observers, and
the French clergyman's originality rendered
them all the more impressive by the fact that
very little has been added by the knowledge to
which we have attained in this matter.   I am
indebted once more to Priestley for the description of the observations.   Perhaps the most interesting feature of this paragraph of Priestley's
account is his emphasis on the caution exercised
by the French clergyman-naturalist to be absolutely sure of his conclusions before he announced them as definitely certain.   A little
more of this same spirit, it might strike the
modern student of physical science, would be an
excellent thing for many of our experimentalists
of the present day.   It seems as though it might
be a decided advantage for a man to have a
good training in matters of conscience, before
taking up physical science, to make him more
careful of his declarations and keep him from
rushing into print with half-baked conclusions
announced as certain, when they are only chance
observations that further investigation so often
shows to be founded on false assumptions.

He took two garden-pots filled with the same earth
and sowed with the same seeds. He kept them constantly in the same place and took the same care of
them, except that one of the two was electrified fifteen
days together for two or three, and sometimes four,

hours a day. The consequence was that the electrified pot always showed the sprouts of its seed two or three days sooner than the other. It also threw out a greater number of shoots, and those longer in a given time; which made him believe that the electric virtue helped to open and display the germs, and thereby to facilitate the growth of plants. This, however, our cautious philosopher only calls a conjecture which required further confirmation. The season, he says, was then too far advanced to allow him to make as many experiments as he could have wished, but he says the next courses of experiments had greater certainty, and they are not less interesting.

Some of his experiments on growing vegetables show with what care he investigated these problems that he had taken up and at the same time illustrate his methods of work. Priestley says that:

He electrified for four or five hours together fruit, green plants, and sponges dipped in water, which he had carefully weighed, and found that, after the experiment, all those bodies were remarkably lighter than others of the same kind, weighed with them both before and after the experiment, and kept in the same place and temperature.

Undoubtedly the most interesting discovery in electricity before Franklin's hypothesis, and the demonstrations as to the identity of lightning and electricity was that of the Leyden Jar. Like many another discovery in science the name is a misnomer. It was called the Leyden Jar or Phial, because originally supposed to have been made by Mr. Cuneus, a native of Leyden, who

was repeating some experiments which he had
seen performed by Professors Muschenboeck and
Alamand in the famous university of that town.
The discovery of the principle on which the Leyden Jar is founded is now generally acknowledged to have been made by Dean Von Kleist
of the Cathedral of Kammin, which, however,
Priestley in his *History* calls Camin. Kammin
is a little town in the Province of Pomerania, in
the distant Eastern part of Prussia, not far from
the Baltic Sea, and situated on what was called
the Kammin Boden near the River Dievenow.
It is about forty miles from Stettin, and probably never has had more than the number of inhabitants which it possesses at the present time,
about 5,000.   In the section of his *History of
Electricity* which concerns the history of the
Leyden Phial itself till Dr. Franklin's discoveries
relating to it, Priestley tells the story of Dean
Von Kleist's discovery in the observant clergyman's own words. These are to be found in the
Register of the Academy at Berlin, to which Von
Kleist's paper had been communicated by the
well-known Dr. Lieberkuhn, of Berlin, to whom
on the fourth of November, 1775, Von Kleist sent
the following account of his discoveries with regard to the accumulation of electricity, and the
serious effects produced, by taking a shock of it
when thus accumulated. This account runs as
follows:

When a nail, or a piece of thick brass wire, etc., is
put into a small apothecary's phial and electrified, re-

markable effects follow, but the phial must be very dry or warm. I commonly rub it over beforehand with a finger on which I put some pounded chalk. If a little mercury or a few drops of spirit of wine be put into it the experiment succeeds the better. As soon as this phial and nail are removed from the electrifying glass, or the prime conductor to which it had been exposed is taken away, it throws out a pencil of flame so long that, with this burning machine in my hand, I have taken above sixty steps in walking about my room. When it is electrified strongly I can take it into another room and there fire spirits of wine with it. If, while it is electrifying, I put my finger on a piece of gold, which I hold in my hand to the nail, I receive a shock which stuns my arms and shoulders.

It is rather amusing, in the light of what we know now of the effects of even a severe shock from a Leyden Jar, to read the accounts of the symptoms noted in themselves by the early observers who received shocks from it. Imagination evidently played a large rôle in the matter. Winckler of Leipzig said that the first time he tried the jar he found great convulsions by it in his body; it put his blood into great agitation; he was afraid of an ardent fever, and was obliged to use refrigerating medicines. He felt a heaviness in his head as if a stone lay upon it. Twice it gave him a bleeding at the nose. After the second shock his wife could scarcely walk, and though a week later, her curiosity stronger than her fears, she tried it once more, it caused her to bleed at the nose only after taking it once. Many men were terrified by it, and even serious professors describe entirely imaginary symptoms.

The jar was taken around Europe for exhibition purposes and did more to awaken popular interest than all the publications of the learned with regard to electricity, in all the preceding centuries. Such is the way of the world.

The French were more interested in science than the Germans, however, at this time. Another French clergyman who experimented on the effects of electricity upon living things during the first half of the eighteenth century was the Abbé Menon, principal of the College of Bueil at Angers. Abbé Menon reached the same conclusions as his more distinguished French colleague, Abbé Nollet. His experiments are mentioned by Priestley (Vol. I, p. 173) and have a special interest of their own. Abbé Menon experimented with many familiar animals and birds. He found that cats, pigeons, and sparrows lost weight when they were constantly under the influence of electrification for six hours or more. He also discovered that the same thing seemed to be true of larger animals, and especially human beings. Instead of concluding as might be expected in a period of such intense interest in electricity that this was due to some marvelous esoteric influence of electrical forces on tissues within the body, or important vital processes, he suggested with a scientific conservatism very creditable at that period, that the reason for the loss in weight was nothing more than an increase in the insensible perspiration of animals. This very cautious conclusion has been confirmed by subsequent investigations. Abbé Menon's conservative declaration can scarcely help but draw additional admiration to him since it was an anticipation in physiology, to some extent at least, as well as in electricity.

One of the very interesting men whose name must be mentioned in the history of electricity at this time, though Priestley does not devote very much space to his work, is Professor George Gordon of Erfurt, who is said to have been a Scotch Benedictine monk. Professor Gordon occupied the chair of philosophy at the University of Erfurt, and he was the first to use a cylinder of glass in order to produce frictional electricity. With these cylinders he was able to produce sparks for experimental purposes much more readily and with more constancy, and in more available form, than had been the case before. His invention added not a little to the possibilities of experimental electricity, since by its means it was possible to have a rather uniform source of electricity for experimental purposes even on unfavorable days. Besides, his instrument was portable and instead of a cake of resin he insulated it by means of a frame furnished with a network of silk.

This Benedictine also invented the Electric Chimes, that is, a series of bells struck by electrical repulsion and attraction, for signal purposes. This has usually been attributed to Franklin, who used such a system of signalling by means of an electric chime in his experiments on lightning. As Brother Potamian has pointed out, however, in his sketch of Franklin in *Makers of Electricity,*[3] in this Franklin was anticipated by Gordon, who has not only a description but also a picture of the apparatus that he employed as an electric chime in his book *An Essay in Explanation of Electricity.*[4] This book by Gordon was published in 1745, whereas Franklin did not use the electric chimes until 1752. At this time Franklin was very familiar with the work that was being done in Europe and especially with what Gordon was accomplishing, for his work was attracting wide attention, and it seems not unlikely that he knew of this apparatus of Gordon's. Of course Franklin makes no claim in the matter, and so it is only a question of tracing the actual priority of observation and invention.

Perhaps in nothing will Father Gordon's ingenuity be better realized than by a recital of the story which is told of his extension of the sources of electricity available for experimental purposes in the laboratory into the animal world. On one occasion, having realized by observations made before that the animal's fur could by appropriate rubbing in favorable weather be made to exhibit very pronounced electrical phenomena, he excited the electricity of " a harmless necessary

[3] *Makers of Electricity*, Fordham University Press, N. Y., 1909.

[4] Versuch Einer Erklärung der Electricität, Erfurt, 1745.

cat " so strongly that when it was conveyed by means of an iron conductor to a little distance from the animal, it fired spirits of wine. A favorite method of experimentation at this time, and one which had been introduced to a considerable extent by Gordon, was the determination of what substances could be set on fire by means of electric sparks. Winckler, for instance, had succeeded in setting fire to French brandy, by means of a spark from his finger when he himself was strongly electrified. Professor Gordon did the still more surprising thing of kindling spirits by means of a jet of electrified water, though the water itself remained cold, of course, and was apparently unaffected by the presence of electricity in it. In a word this Scotch Benedictine was another of those inquiring minds who in the garb of monks and priests did experimental work of a high order during the decade or two just before Franklin's discovery, and led up to the development of electricity which came during the subsequent century and a half.

Nor did the interest of Catholic clergymen in the science of electricity, nor their success in bringing about new developments of it, cease after the discoveries made by Franklin and the wide extension of the interest in the science which brought so many investigators into the field. Volta, who did so much at the end of the eighteenth century and the beginning of the nineteenth, had been a clerical student and remained all during his life in close touch with his

clerical friends.   Galvani, who because of his
delicacy of conscience which made him refuse to
take the oath to the new government that had
been established in Italy with the connivance of
Napoleon, was said to be more a monk than a
layman, and who was indeed buried in the habit
of the Third Order of St. Francis, is another of
the distinguished contributors to the science at
this time.   The third great name in science at
the end of the century is that of the Abbé Haüy,
better known as the Father of Crystallography
than for his contributions to electrical science,
but whose investigations into the property of
crystals and certain electrical phenomena which
they display under varying conditions of temperature, merited for him also the title of the father
of pyro-electricity.   Professor Chrystal in the
introduction to his article on Electricity in the
Encyclopedia Britannica (Ninth Edition) in the
historical review of the development of the
science says:

> But it was reserved for the Abbé Haüy to throw a
> clear light on this curious branch of the science.   He
> found that the electricity of the tourmaline decreased
> rapidly from the summits or poles towards the center-
> middle of the center of the crystal, where it was im-
> perceptible; and he discovered that when a tourmaline
> is broken into any number of fragments, each fragment
> when excited has two opposite poles.   Haüy discovered
> the same property in the Siberian and Brazilian topaz,
> borate of magnesia, mesotype, prehnite, sphene and
> calamine.   He also found that the polarity which min-
> erals receive from heat has a relation to the secondary
> forms of their crystals—the tourmaline, for example,

having its resinous pole at the summit of the crystal which has three faces and its vitreous pole at the summit which has six faces. In the other pyro-electrical crystals above mentioned Haüy detected the same deviation from the rules of symmetry in their secondary crystals which occurs in tourmaline.[5]

Indeed this chapter of what Catholic clergymen accomplished for the developing science of electricity, before it became the formal department of knowledge which was to be studied in the universities and be the subject of academic attention generally, is the best possible proof of the readiness of the clerical mind to follow clues of original investigation in the problems of nature and to turn quite naturally to Nature Study. In their hours of leisure these men developed a deep interest in the wonderful phenomena of magnetism and electrical manifestations generally. They set themselves to find the reason for these manifestations and so laid the foundation of our modern electricity. To them more than to any other set of men, even the university professors of the time, is due its development. They could not have employed their leisure more interestingly for themselves nor as the outcome proved more beneficially for mankind. This chapter in the development of electrical science should be a definite response to the argument so often advanced that clergymen are prevented by their acceptance of so many truths on faith from having such an

[5] See *Catholic Churchmen in Science,* first series, for a full sketch of Abbé Haüy's life.

openness of mind as would enable them to be original discoverers or investigators in science. The very opposite proves to be the case, for in proportion to their numbers more of them devoted themselves to the asking of questions of nature than from among any other class of educated people of the time, and their patient, humble investigation in the true spirit of science was, as we have seen, marvelously successful.   Faith they had, but also the scientific spirit in a supreme degree, and they added gloriously to science!

VII.

THE JESUIT ASTRONOMERS.

THE heavens shew forth the glory of God, and the firmament declareth the work of His hands.—Ps. 18: 1.

THE passing fever of scientific thought in its birth-throes which threatens sound doctrine and has nothing to put in its place, will calm down as it always has heretofore.—JEAN BAPTISTE DUMAS.

THE JESUIT ASTRONOMERS.

CATHOLICS who know the realities of the Galileo case have grown tired of explaining that the famous trial of the great Italian astronomer is an historical incident almost entirely personal in character, an exception to the general rule of the relationship of the Popes to science, and absolutely no index of the policy of the Popes or of the Church toward things scientific, and, above all, toward astronomy. In spite of this view, so well established by the most careful and complete research, the Galileo affair is constantly assumed by Protestant writers, and, of course, by the Protestant public generally, to be the keynote of the Papal attitude to science—the one fact from which all history may be judged. Cardinal Newman once said that the Galileo case was the exception that proved the rule of beneficent patronage of science uniformly exhibited by the Church authorities. It is " the one stock argument to the contrary." Professor Augustus de Morgan, in his article on " The Motion of the Earth " in the *English Encyclopedia,* an authority not likely to be suspected of Catholic sympathies, has expressed exactly this same conclusion.

" The Papal power," he says, " must upon the whole have been moderately used in matters of philosophy, if we may judge by the great stress

laid on this one case of Galileo. It is the standing proof that an authority which has lasted a
thousand years was all the time occupied in
checking the progress of thought! There are
certainly one or two other instances, but those
who make most of the outcry do not know them."
Professor Huxley, writing to St. George Mivart,
12 November, 1885, says that, after looking into
the Galileo case while he was on the ground in
Italy, he had arrived at the conclusion that "the
Pope and the College of Cardinals had rather
the best of it." In our own time M. Bertrand,
the perpetual secretary of the French Academy
of Sciences, declared that "the great lesson for
those who would wish to oppose reason with vio-
lence was clearly to be read in Galileo's story,
and the scandal of his condemnation was brought
about without any profound sorrow to Galileo
himself; and his long life, considered as a whole,
must be looked upon as the most serene and en-
viable in the history of science." [1] Any one who
knows the circumstances refuses any longer to
accept the significance so usually given the Galileo case by writers who must find material in opposition to the Church.

I have thought, however, that since the Galileo
case has been taken in many minds to show that
the Church was opposed to the development of
science, and especially to the progress of astronomy, that a presentation of another phase of the

[1] See Appendix, *Popes and Science*, Fordham University Press, 1908.

history of astronomical science during the century preceding and following the Galileo incident might be of service as showing the true attitude of the Church toward astronomy and astronomers. In every department of science that I have had to investigate, where there has been question on the part of Protestant historians of opposition by the Church authorities to the development of a particular science, I have always found that the reason for the confident assertion they make as to Church opposition to science is that they are ignorant of the real history of the science in question.

A typical example is to be found in the views held by many writers with regard to surgery. Surgery is supposed to be a recent development in the history of science, because during the Middle Ages the Church set itself in direct opposition to the development of anatomy in such a way as to prevent that evolution of surgery which must depend on accurate anatomical knowledge. President Andrew D. White, formerly professor of history at Cornell, summing up what many others have said before him, declares in his *History of the Warfare of Science with Theology in Christendom,* that as a consequence of this attitude of the Church toward surgery, surgery did not develop at all during the Middle Ages. He even goes farther and declares that " so deeply was the idea (of the sacredness of the human body) rooted in the mind of the Universal Church that for over a thousand years

surgery was considered dishonorable; the greatest monarchs were often unable to secure an
ordinary surgical operation, and it was only in
1406 that a better beginning was made, when the
Emperor Wenzel of Germany ordered that dis-
honor should no longer attach to the surgical
profession."

This paragraph, as I have shown in my chapter
on " The Church and Surgery" in the volume
The Popes and Science,[2] probably contains more
arrant nonsense with regard to surgery and its
history than one might think could possibly be
compressed into so short a space. The thirteenth and fourteenth centuries, far from being
periods barren of surgical development, constitute the most fruitful epoch in the history of surgery down to our own time. Gurlt, the great
German historian of surgery, has devoted some
three hundred pages of the first volume of his
authoritative *History of Surgery in Middle and
Western Europe,* to the period when President
White so calmly tells us there was no surgery
in Europe. Professor Pagel, another German
authority on the history of medicine, has devoted
much attention to this time, and tells us that " a
more favorable star shone over surgery than
over medicine during the Middle Ages." All the
authorities are agreed in declaring this time to
be much more important in the history of surgery than many of the succeeding centuries.

[2] *The Popes and Science,* Fordham University Press,
New York, 1908.

President White knows nothing of the history of surgery at this time, and assumes that there was none.

Just this same state of affairs exists with regard to other sciences, as I have already said. A typical example is to be found in the history of astronomy. Those who exaggerate the significance of the Galileo case declare that the reason why astronomy did not develop before this time was that the Church was so unalterably opposed to it that its development was seriously hampered, if not actually prevented. They say this so confidently that ordinary readers are sure that they must know that there was no development of astronomy before Galileo's time. As a matter of fact, there is a very rich history of astronomy for several centuries before Galileo. There is no doubt that he was a great genius, who illuminated his favorite science; there is no doubt either that his example inspired many other investigators to do great work, and that his discoveries ushered in a new and wonderful period in astronomical science; but to say that there was no astronomy before Galileo, or that the subject had not been pursued seriously and very fruitfully by many profound students, is quite as egregious a mistake as to say that surgery did not develop down to the beginning of the fifteenth century.

As a matter of fact, astronomy had developed very wonderfully before Galileo's time, and some of the men whose names are greatest in that science had made their contributions to it during centuries long before the seventeenth. Among them deserves to be mentioned Albertus Magnus, whose contributions to physical geography and to the general state of information with regard to the rotundity of the earth and the existence of the antipodes must be considered as representing the foundation of modern astronomy. His great contemporary, Roger Bacon, worked out the theory of lenses, and suggested that light moved at a definite velocity, thus adding his quota to the foundation of astronomy. It was in the fifteenth century, however, that the beginnings of astronomy in our modern sense came, and the father of modern observation in astronomy is Regiomontanus. After him the great name in the science of the stars is, of course, Copernicus, and with him the newest phase in the development of astronomical science begins.[3]

The interesting feature about the work of all these men is that it was accomplished during the leisure afforded them by their occupations as clergymen. All of these men were faithful sons of the Church and were proud and happy to recognize her as their mother. Albertus Magnus has received the honors of beatification. Regiomontanus, having been brought down to Rome by the Popes in order to correct the calendar, so impressed himself upon the ecclesiastical authorities in the Papal capital that he was made the

[3] See sketch of Copernicus in first volume of *Catholic Churchmen in Science*.

Bishop of Ratisbon, succeeding after two centuries that other great ecclesiastical scientist,
Albertus Magnus, in this see. Copernicus was
the canon of the Cathedral at Frauenberg, a personal friend of his Bishop, who devoted himself
to the help of his Bishop in keeping that diocese
in the Catholic fold during the stormy times of
Luther's revolt in Germany, when the dioceses
all round them were going over to Lutheranism.

All this shows that surely there was no opposition between the Church and astronomy, but,
on the contrary, that men were held in high estimation for their astronomical knowledge and
received preferment in the Church as a consequence of it. One great churchman, Cardinal
Nicholas, of Cusa, who was very close to the
councils of the Papacy during the fifteenth century and who was commissioned to make such
reforms as were needed in Germany, was also
distinguished for his advanced thinking with regard to astronomical questions, and, as pointed
out by Janssen in the first volume of his *History
of the German People,* declared that " the earth
moves like the other stars," and other teachings
that are supposed to be distant from such men's
thoughts at that time.

The Galileo case is not the culmination of organized effort by ecclesiastical authority against
astronomy. Of any such policy there is not a
trace to be found anywhere. There is, moreover, another way of looking at the significance
of the Galileo case, on the background of what

was being done for astronomy by churchmen
just before and after this time, that constitutes
an even more striking contradiction of the impressions that many people derive from this
famous historical trial, and try to impress upon
others. This is the relation of the priests of the
Society of Jesus, the great teaching Order established just about a century before Galileo's trial
in 1534, and into whose hands were gradually
falling the best opportunities for education in
Europe about the time that Galileo became prominent. The Jesuits were closely attached to the
Pope. The idea of their founder was that they
should be a special Papal soldiery, ready always
to go wherever the Pope sent them, taking a
special vow to this effect, and trained to think of
themselves as the Pope's closest servants. During the century before and after the Galileo trial
they were looked upon by all of Europe as
in closer communion with the policy of the
Papacy and as representing Papal thought and
influence more than any other set of men.

It so happened that very early in the history
of this Order its members became interested in
astronomy. Their teaching of the studious
youth of Europe tempted them to be leaders in
research in this great scientific department as
well as in classical education. It was the one
phase in physical science that was developing in
the sixteenth and seventeenth centuries, with that
strict scientific method and thoroughgoing investigation and observation that characterize

modern science. The Jesuits devoted themselves
to it not only with enthusiasm, but with a success that has written their names large over all
the history of astronomy for three centuries.
Every single advance in astronomy saw the work
of some Jesuit contributing to the conclusions
that were finally reached. In many departments
the original initiative came from them, and the
intimate communication between their various
houses brought about a wide diffusion of the
enthusiasm for study that was of the greatest
possible benefit for the rising science. Nearly
every important Jesuit college had an observatory, in which good work was being done,
and all the great secular investigators in science
were glad to be in touch with the Jesuits, to
write and receive letters from them, and in general to acknowledge that this body of clergymen
was a world-wide academy of astronomers with
whose work it was necessary to be in touch if
one would keep himself *au courant* with astronomical progress.

Modern historians of astronomy and writers
on the development of the science have not been
slow to admit how much was done for their scientific department by the Jesuits. It is scarcely
in Germany, however, that one would look for
significant tributes to the successful devotion of
the Jesuits to science, yet in recent years science
has come to obliterate international prejudice
and to smooth international feelings, and so it
is not so surprising as it might otherwise be that

it should also obliterate religious bigotry and intolerance. Bearing this in mind, a recent expression of Professor Foster, the director of the astronomical observatory at Berlin, in which he gives due credit to the Jesuit astronomers, past and present, will not be so surprising as it might otherwise be. In the *Quarterly Journal of the German Astronomical Society* for 1890 Professor Foster said:[4] " Among the members of the Society of Jesus in the past and in the present we find so many excellent astronomers, and in general so many investigators of purest scientific devotion, that it is of important interest to their colleagues in science to notice them."

This tribute from Protestant Germany, in which for twenty years before its utterance the Jesuits had not been allowed to teach, and from which they had been driven so ruthlessly by a German Government that called the movement it was engaged in when it banished them a *Kulturkampf*—as if it were a struggle for culture and education—is the best possible evidence of how Jesuit scientists have won even their enemies to admiration of their accomplishments. The compliment may serve, indeed, as an introduction to what the Jesuits did for astronomy, though it must not be taken to mean that the members of the Order did not devote themselves to other forms of science. Their names occur in every branch of science. They began their

[4] " Vierteljahreschrift der Astronomische Geschellschaft," 1890, page 60.

existence only in the middle of the sixteenth century, for more than a half century after 1773
they were not in existence, and yet the number
of distinguished scientists in the Order is simply
marvelous. Poggendorf's *Biographical Dictionary of the Exact Sciences* contains in its first
two volumes the names of 8,847 savants from
remote antiquity until the year 1863. Amongst
these names a little more than ten per cent are
those of Catholic clergymen. This number is
magnificently significant of the attitude of the
Church to science, if we only reflect that clergymen take up science as a favorite avocation, while
for most scientific discoverers the pursuit of science was in some form their vocation in life.
Most of them belonged to professions which
obliged them to devote themselves to the exact
sciences, and they were teachers of physics and
mathematics, chemists, hydrographers, engineers,
nautical authorities, and the like. Clergymen
took up science, however, as a pleasure, not a
task that they were bound to do.

Science, then, has been a favorite avocation
for a great many clergymen, and they have pursued it with marked success. Amongst nearly
1,000 Catholic clergymen who have been distinguished in the domain of the exact sciences
the Jesuits number nearly fifty per cent. Among
the great number of men of all kinds who have
proved themselves successful in the pursuit of
science the Jesuits during the short space of two
and a half centuries of existence have succeeded

in placing about one out of twenty of all the men who were to be remembered by succeeding generations for attainments in science. For a society that was founded to carry out the will of the Papacy as exactly as possible, that has always devoted itself to the fulfillment of this object with exemplary fidelity, to have given this large number of men to science is the best possible answer to any pretense that the Popes or the Church were opposed in any way to scientific development.

Almost from the very beginning of their history, as I have said, the Jesuits applied themselves with the liveliest interest and with corresponding success to the study of astronomical problems. Within twenty-five years of the foundation of the order some distinguished astronomical observers had developed among them. At the beginning of the seventeenth century, when the Order was as yet scarcely more than half a century old, they were in correspondence with the great astronomers of the time—Kepler and Galileo—and were looked upon as wonderfully successful students and indeed distinguished authorities of the time in astronomy. Already many of them had made original contributions of high order to various departments of this science, and it came to be a tradition that some of the best men in the Order should be constantly assigned to the task of keeping up Jesuit prestige in astronomical researches. De Backer's *Library of Writers of the Society of*

CHRISTOPHER CLAVIUS, S. J.

Jesus [5] shows that over 200 writers among the Jesuits have made important contributions to astronomical literature. [6]

The first Jesuit to attract world-wide attention for his attainments in astronomy, and especially the mathematics relating to it, was the famous Father Clavius, to whom Pope Gregory XIII entrusted the reformation of the Calendar. The Gregorian Calendar, which was then substituted for the Julian Calendar, so thoroughly corrects the tendency of the formal year to depart from the solar year that there will be a difference of a day in the reckoning only once in some three thousand five hundred years. By making every fourth thousand year, then, an exception to the ordinary rule with regard to intercalary days, even this tendency may be so overcome that

[5] De Backer's *Bibliothèque des Écrivains de la Comp. de Jésus,* Paris, 1876.

[6] The material for this article has been largely derived from the papers on Jesuit astronomy written for *Popular Astronomy* by Father William F. Rigge, S.J., of Creighton University Observatory, Omaha, Nebraska. The first of these papers, on the "Jesuit Astronomy of the Old Society," is a translation by Father Rigge of Father Johann Schreiber's article on the Jesuits of the seventeenth and eighteenth centuries and their relation to astronomy, published in the German periodical, *Natur und Offenbarung* ("Nature and Revelation"), Vol. XLIX., 1903. Father Johann Schreiber, S.J., was for years the assistant astronomer at the Haynald Observatory of the Jesuits at Kalocsa, Hungary. His death, 10 March, 1903, deprived the scientific world of a distinguished worker.

further correction will not be needed for a term of nearly one hundred thousand years. Under ordinary circumstances, then, this will amply suffice to keep the computation of human time in sufficiently close relationship to that of celestial time, and the ease with which the difficult problem was solved only serves to show how well it had been studied out and how ingeniously the great Jesuit mathematician had succeeded in reaching an expression in very simple terms for correction purposes.

While we speak of Father Clavius as having corrected the Calendar, of course it must not be understood that the world had waited until this period to recognize the error that had taken place in the computation of time or had made no previous attempt to correct it. Albert the Great had called attention to the error and had made some suggestions with regard to it. Roger Bacon, the great Franciscan of the thirteenth century seems even to have reached the solution of the difficulty, and to have made definite suggestions to the Pope as to how the correction could be made, though the world was not yet ready for this great scientific advance. Great ecclesiastical scientists in the succeeding centuries were also interested in the problem, and it was evidently only a question of time until there should be a definite move in the matter.

Cardinal Nicholas, of Cusa, the great ecclesiastical scientist and mathematician wrote a book on this subject during the first half of the fifteenth century. About the middle of this same century Regiomontanus was summoned to Rome with the definite purpose of correcting the calendar, but unfortunately fell ill and died within a few months, so that the great task was not accomplished. For the next century the subject was often in the minds of the prominent ecclesiastics, and it was evidently only a question of time till it should be done under the auspices of the Church.

Unfortunately for the modern world in many ways the actual correction of the Calendar did not become an accomplished fact until after the movement that has now come to be known by historians generally as the Religious Revolt in Germany, at the beginning of the sixteenth century. As a consequence of this most of the Northern nations, especially the Teutonic peoples, had become separated from the Church, and absolutely refused to accept anything, even a correction of the Calendar founded on scientific principles at the hands of the Pope. Most of them preferred for centuries to be wrong on an important scientific matter rather than be right with the Pope. In England, owing to religious intolerance, the correction of the Calendar did not come until the middle of the eighteenth century, and then the incident aroused such bitter religious feelings that many people attributed certain visitations of disease and great calamities to the taking-away of eleven days from them, and a mob patroled the streets of

London demanding that the days should be given back to them. Russia has always refused to accept the correction and prefers to differ from all the rest of the world and suffer all the inconveniences of having a special date of her own rather than to be right at the suggestion of the Popes.

Besides the correction of the Calendar, though it is not generally known, we owe also to Father Clavius the invention of that important instrument, the Vernier, without which it would be so difficult to make many of the exact observations of all kinds in laboratories. This little instrument consists incidentally of two measuring scales moving upon one another and so arranged that one of them is separated into ten divisions, to which correspond nine divisions of the other, so that measurements can be read to tenths of the unit employed, whether that be an inch or a centimeter or a degree of an angle. Until comparatively recent years the invention of this extremely useful appliance has been attributed to either Nonius or Vernier. Brencing, however, in an article on " Nonius or Vernier " in the *Astronomische Nachrichten,*[1] says: " Clavius has been forgotten or neglected in an unintelligible way. I was surprised when I came upon the following passages in his works, which give the clearest proof that we are indebted to no other than Clavius for the theory of vernier sub-division as well for linear as for circular measure-

[1] Vol. XCVI., page 131.

ment. They have been overlooked." He then quotes in full the passages which prove his assertion.

After Father Clavius, the most distinguished Jesuit worker in astronomy was Father Christopher Scheiner, who died about 1650. He was one of the first, if not actually the first, to discover sun-spots, in March, 1611, and from that time on he observed them uninterruptedly, organizing a corps of observers, all Jesuits, to observe simultaneously in many other places. How wide this chain of observers was as the result of the spread of the Order will be appreciated from the list, which shows Father Cysatus working at Ingolstadt, Father Gall in Lisbon, Portugal, Father Schönberger in Freiburg, Father Ruess in the West Indies, Father Malapertius in Belgium, and Father Biancani in Parma. Father Scheiner's observations were made mainly upon the sun. He was the first to apply the so-called dark glasses that are now generally used and the first to invent the artifice of placing a diaphram over the objective. He succeeded in collecting a truly wonderful amount of information regarding the sun, considering the inadequate means at his command. It has even been declared by good authorities that except for spectroscopy and photography, solar researches have not yielded anything in recent years that cannot be found in Scheiner's observations.

All that he had discovered with regard to the sun was published in a great work, under the

title *Rosa Ursina,* in 1631. The German astronomer Winecke declared thirty years ago in the
German *Quarterly of the Astronomical Society* [8]
that " in his *Rosa Ursina* Scheiner established
truths that have been forgotten because this early
observer was wantonly set aside, and then these
once discovered truths had to be found out anew
in our time." It is with regard to sun-spots
particularly that Scheiner's work shows his wonderful powers of observation. He had mastered
very thoroughly the formation and dissolution
of the spots. The word *faculæ* comes from him. He
had formed ideas about the physical constitution
of the sun very like those of to-day, and he even
surmised that the interior of the sun, the nucleus
or kernel, might have a rotational velocity different from that of the outer shell.

It is not surprising that Father Scheiner's
greatest pupil, Father Cysatus, should have made
some magnificent observations. He was the first
to use a telescope on a comet. This was the
comet of 1618. Wolff, in the *History of Astronomy,* says that " his [Cysatus'] paper on this
comet, published in the *Mathemata Astronomica*
of Ingolstadt in 1619, is justly numbered among
the most important papers of former times concerning comets." One very wonderful thing in
the paper is that Cysatus shows that he had
found a curvature in the orbit of the planet
which had been supposed to be a straight line,
and he declares that this would be a phenomenon

[8] *Vierteljahreschrift der Astr. Ges.,* 1878,

of great importance if it could be confirmed by
further observation. He would not trust himself, however, to come to a conclusion in the
matter, so little was the deviation from a straight
line, which yet did not escape his acute powers
of observation. His description of comets remains classical down to our own day. After
comets he turned his attention to nebulæ. They
seemed to him to furnish an explanation of the
structure of the comet's head. Cysatus was the
first to mention not only the nebula of Orion,
but also the so-called trapezium, that is, the stars
that are compressed into a very narrow space in
this nebula. This discovery is generally ascribed
to Huygens, but there is no doubt that Cysatus
had seen this phenomenon and described it many
years before the Dutch astronomer.

Early in the seventeenth century the Jesuits
began to make interesting and important observations on the stars. Father Zupi was the first
to describe the dark stripes or bands which are
to be found on Jupiter. He was also the first to
see the phases of Mercury which Galileo surmised more than saw, and he furnished accurate
drawing of this manifestation. Father Grimaldi
carefully studied Saturn, and determined very
closely its oblateness.

The name of a great Jesuit astronomer is connected quite as closely with our knowledge of
the moon as are the names of brother Jesuits
with the sun. Father Riccioli introduced the
lunar nomenclature, which is in use even to-day

and which has lessened the labor of the memory
in locating the lunar formations. His colleague,
Father Grimaldi, drew up one of the first maps
of the moon worthy of the name. This was published in the year 1651 in Father Riccioli's *Almagest*. Wolff, in his *Handbook of Astronomy,*
says that the merits of this map have been much
underestimated. It is in some particulars superior in completeness and accuracy even to
Hevelius's map. Riccioli described the surface
of the moon, and Wolff says that his remarks
as to the probable nature of the surface are
juster than those of most of his immediate successors. Both himself and Father Grimaldi occupied themselves with observations of the libra-
tion of the moon. Their published observations
in this matter would make a good-sized book.
They were closely in touch with Hevelius at this
time, and the epistolary correspondence of these
three astronomers contains some interesting passages.

The most important literary work of the
Jesuits during the seventeenth century was the
Almagestum Novum, written by Father J. B.
Riccioli and published at Bologna in 1653. Ptolemy's great work on astronomy, which was the
text-book of Europe for fifteen hundred years,
is usually called, because of its Arabian designation, the *Almagest*. Father Riccioli took a very
ambitious name then. Von Littrow made little of
the value of the work. Distinguished authorities, however, have agreed in designating the *Al-*

magestum Novum as the pandect of astronomical knowledge. It is a colossal work, and yet its author's modest object, as stated in the preface, was mainly to provide ready information for brother Jesuit astronomers. His idea was to make " an astronomical work which may be a kind of library for the men of our Society and for others who cannot have access to the great number of such books or the leisure to read them —a work in which I have collected with the greatest fullness the whole of the old and the new astronomy, together with the controversies that occurred therein." This work is all the more valuable because it contains, perhaps, for the first time in the history of book-making, an index, in which all the persons mentioned in the book are named and the data of their lives, together with the pages on which references to their work occurs.[9]

[9] Von Littrow's unjustified criticism of Father Riccioli's work is a reminder that occasionally one finds such prejudice existing among astronomical historians, and that the work of the Jesuits, because of intolerance, is not given its due place. It scarcely seems possible that the history of science would be thus disfigured, but it is. Professor Simon Newcomb, one of our best authorities on mathematical astronomy in this country, has vindicated Father Maximilian Hell, the Jesuit, against the misrepresentations of Von Littrow in the astronomical papers of *The American Ephemeris,* Vol. II., pages 301-302. He says: " The conclusion was reached that Littrow's inferences were entirely at fault. Littrow's mistakes were due to the fact that he was color blind to red, in consequence of which he

Among the most noteworthy incidents in the story of the Jesuits's relations to astronomy is probably to be found in their relations to Kepler, the astronomer to whom we owe the laws that form the basis of modern astronomy. Kepler was, indeed, upon the very best terms with the Jesuits and continued to be so all his life. The great mathematical astronomer had been expelled by the Lutherans from the University of Tübingen and excommunicated by one of the Lutheran pastors at Linz. When the Emperor of Austria, however, issued a decree banishing all Protestant professors from the Austrian universities, Kepler was exempted by name and continued to occupy the chair of astronomy at the University of Gratz, and it was well understood that it was mainly through the influence of the Jesuits that the exception in his favor was made. There are a number of letters extant which passed between Kepler and the Jesuits, and especially a communication with regard to astrology, in which Kepler expressed his belief in this illusion, addressed to Fathers Serrarius and Ziegler, in Mainz. The date of this was 18 October, 1606, twenty-five years before the condemnation of Galileo.

It is very evident that during the half century in which Galileo's work was done—from 1600 to 1650—the Jesuits were not only not hampered at all by their ecclesiastical superiors in the study

wholly misjudged the case on first examining the manuscript, and afterwards saw everything from the point of view of a prosecuting attorney."

of astronomy, but must have been encouraged
in every way. We find them at work not in one
or two places, but in every part of the world
where there was an opportunity. We find them
engaged not on a few academic problems, but on
every phase of scientific progress in astronomy.
The sun, the moon, the stars, the comets, all the
heavenly bodies come in for their attention, and
with regard to every one of these subjects work
done by the Jesuits constitutes an important
chapter in the history of astronomy. Very probably if their work had not been done, others
would have been found to do it, but as a matter
of fact no other body of men connected by any
bond in history accomplished so much for astronomy at this time as they did. They were in epistolary correspondence with most of the distinguished astronomical observers of the time, and
were looked upon by these men as respected colleagues and worthy workers in the same great
cause.

The policy of the first half of the seventeenth
century was to be continued during the next 125
years, until the suppression of the Jesuits. Humboldt, in his *Kosmos*, at the beginning of the
nineteenth century, writes: " I drew attention to
the fact that Alpha of the Southern Cross is one
of those stars whose multiple nature was first
recognized in 1681 and 1687 by the Jesuits Fon-
taney, Noel, and Richaud. This early recognition of binary systems," he adds, " is the more
remarkable as Lacaille seventy years later did

not describe Alpha Crucis as a double star. Richaud also discovered the binary character of Alpha Centauri almost simultaneously with that of Alpha Crucis and fully nineteen years before the voyage of Feuillée, to whom Henderson erroneously attributed the discovery." This beginning of work on the double stars was to be continued with marvelous success by their Jesuit colleagues during the next century. It was Father Christian Mayer, S.J., working at Mannheim, who made the double stars a subject of special research. He expressly stated that " the smaller stars, which are so near the larger, are either illuminated naturally dark planets, or that both of these cosmic bodies, the principal star and its companion (the word *comes* which he used for this has since become classic) are self-luminous suns revolving around each other. That any fraternal solidarity did not influence their astronomical opinions can be appreciated from the fact that some of Father Mayer's teaching with regard to the double stars was rather strenuously assailed by Father Maximilian Hell, S.J., himself a distinguished astronomer and director of the Imperial Observatory of Vienna.

During the eighteenth century the work done by the Jesuit astronomers at the Imperial Observatory of Vienna attracted widespread attention. Father Maximilian Hell, whom we have already mentioned, issued about thirty separate publications. He edited the astronomical *Ephemerides,* in which the progress in astronomy was noted

for nearly thirty years, and was succeeded in
this editorial office by Father Triesnecker. The
observations of the Jesuit astronomers at Vienna
on the transit of Venus of 1761 are among the
most valuable recorded. They were in correspondence at this time with Jesuits in many parts
of the world.

One of the most distinguished contributors
to astronomical science among the Jesuits during
the eighteenth century was Father Roger Boscovich. We owe to him seventy rather important
publications. Most of these are on astronomical
subjects. One on gravitation attracted wide attention. Another on the determination of the
orbits of comets, and another on the annual ab-
errations of fixed stars, are mentioned especially
by Houzeau in his *Vademecum de l'Astronomia,*
which is usually considered one of the best bib-
liographical guides in astronomical literature.
Father Boscovich did his work at Rome, and his
opinions were frequently quoted everywhere as
of authority. His work, and especially his suggestions with regard to the measurements of terrestrial arcs, and his opinions as to the most
probable value of the ellipticity of the earth from
the results of all the measurements accessible to
him, represented for geodesy, according to Wolff
in his *Handbook of Astronomy,* " the dawn of a
new day."

Probably for our modern time the most interesting popular phase of the success of the Jesuits
in their devotion to astronomy is the number of

ingenious instruments which they invented. Usually it would not be expected that such serious students devoted to book-learning would have much success as mechanical inventors. While we might not be surprised at their accomplishments as observers, as mathematical calculators, and as authors in astronomical matters, the invention of instruments would surely seem to be out of their line. We have already seen, however, that one of the most important adjustments for scientific instruments, the vernier, is the invention of Father Clavius, though called, as is the case with many another invention, by some one else's name. It is to them also that we owe the equatorial mounting of telescopes, by which the telescope, being turned about an axis parallel to the earth, enables one always to keep a star in the field of view without difficulty, once the tube has been set upon it. This invention is derived from a contrivance of the Tyrolese Father Christopher Grienberger, who died at Rome in 1636. Father Scheiner is the inventor of the first astronomical telescope—that is, one consisting of convex glasses exclusively, the telescope in use before this, the so-called Dutch telescope, having both concave and convex glasses. The improved Jesuit telescope has so many advantages that it entirely superseded the older form. Father Scheiner is also the inventor of the pantograph for the reproduction of drawings to scale which is so generally used to-day.

The idea of a reflecting telescope also comes

from a Jesuit, and, curiously enough, was suggested by a young man scarcely more than twenty years of age, Father Nicholas Zucchi, who carried out the idea so far that he took the image made by a concave mirror and examined it with a concave lense. The idea of using the circular field formed by the last diaphragm in the telescope as a micrometer, called a ring micrometer, was the happy invention of Father Boscovich toward the end of the eighteenth century. Father Kircher, the distinguished Jesuit scientist and collector, after whom the Kircherian Museum at Rome is named, was the inventor of an apparatus for demonstrating to students the relative positions of the planets and the sun. He is also the inventor of what we now know as the magic lantern, the idea for which came from another Jesuit, but was developed by Father Kircher for teaching purposes.

Since the refoundation of the Jesuits at the beginning of the nineteenth century the same devotion to astronomy has characterized the Order as before the suppression. One might think that in view of the supreme devotion of the generations of the nineteenth century to science and the success that has resulted, the work of the Jesuits would be entirely overshadowed. This has not proved to be the case, however. On the contrary, in many parts of the world they have accomplished so much by original investigation of superior merit in subjects of all kinds relating to the heavens as to attract wide-spread attention.

One of the greatest astronomers of the century was among their number. The work done at their observatories at Rome; at Stonyhurst, England; at Georgetown, in the United States, and at Kalocsa, in Hungary, has held the eyes of the astronomical world. In Havana and in Manila, their observations in meteorology have added new chapters to this science, and have proved the basis for practical advances in the foretelling of tropical storms that have saved thousands of lives and an immense amount of property. Their work has been thoroughly appreciated by the United States Government, at whose expense the observations made by the Jesuits in Manila have been published for the benefit of the world, since the Jesuits were without the means of publishing them.

The greatest exemplar of what the Jesuits did in astronomy came in the nineteenth century— indeed, so close to our own time that the memory of his work and accomplishment does not need to be recalled to many of our scientists, and especially astronomers, who followed it in the course of its accomplishment. Father Angelo Secchi, the head of the Roman observatory, was probably the greatest astronomer of the second half of the nineteenth century. He is the father of astronomical spectroscopy and one of the most ingenious of men, of almost unexampled devotion to his astronomical observations, and marvelous success in the applications of his work to science and to teaching. All our modern text-

ANGELO SECCHI, S. J.

books of astronomy not only mention his name
with reverence, but still use his theories and his
illustrations for teaching purposes. To quote
from an unpublished manuscript sketch of Father
Secchi's life by Father Rigge, S.J.: [10] " Simon
Newcomb, who is acknowledged by all to be at
present the world's greatest mathematical astronomer, devotes considerable space in his text-book
of *Popular Science* to what he calls Secchi's
first theory and Secchi's later theory of sun-spots.
Langley, in his *New Astronomy,* gives a number
of Secchi's illustrations. Secchi's typical sun-
spot as well as other figures still appear in every
popular, no less than in every technical, treatise
on the sun."

It was with regard to the sun that Father
Secchi's greatest work was done. His text-book,
Le Soliel, written in French and printed in Paris
in 1870, is the fundamental treatise for our
knowledge of the sun during the nineteenth century. Every book written on the sun since quotes
it, and its illustrations are largely drawn upon
even at the present time. It was translated into
most modern languages and became the standard
work on the subject. Besides his work on sun-
spots, in which Father Secchi was a modern

[10] This sketch is to be published later in a series of
Makers of Astronomy, which, like *The Makers of Medicine* and *The Makers of Electricity,* will serve to
bring out very clearly that the great minds of science,
far from being unbelieving, were profound and even
devout believers.

pioneer, his observations on the corona of the
sun during eclipses, and especially his photographs
of this subject, place him among the great original contributors to our astronomical knowledge.
In his own time his observations were considered
the best of their kind that had ever been made,
and far ahead of anything that had been accomplished before.

The critical examination and classification of
the spectra of 4,000 stars entailed an enormous
amount of work.   One would think that the observations for this would occupy a lifetime.
Father Secchi was thoroughly convinced, however, that it was no use making observations
unless they were thoroughly recorded and made
available for others.   His literary work in astronomy, then, is almost incredible.   He sent nearly
700 communications to forty-two journals.   Over
300 of these appeared in the *Comptes Rendues*
and in the *Astromische Nachrichten,* the French
and German journals of astronomy that are the
authoritative records of scientific work.   Besides this he wrote five books, the one on the
sun we have already mentioned, a second on the
stars was published in Milan in 1877, a third
was on *Cosmography,* a fourth was on *The Unity
of the Physical Forces,* and a fifth, a posthu-
mous work, on *The Elements of Terrestrial Physics.*   The titles of his productions, without com-
ment and without repetition, cover the amazing
number of nineteen pages quarto in double col-

umns of Summervogel's *Bibliothèque de la Compagnie de Jésus.*[11]

While his name is irrevocably attached to the development of the astronomy of the sun, Father Secchi made observations of great value on every form of heavenly body, and almost on every object that can be seen in the skies.   He made frequent measurements of the heights of the mountains of the moon and called attention to many special features of its surface.   He examined all the planets diligently, and was one of the first to see the so-called canals on Mars and to observe Jupiter's third satellite as spotted.   " He made many spectroscopic observations on the comets and examined carefully the spectra of nebulæ, meteors, and auroras.   It was with regard to the fixed stars more than to any other class of heavenly bodies, possibly more even than to the sun itself, that Father Secchi has won for himself an undying name.   Besides measuring innumerable positions of double stars (Gledhill's *Double Stars* mentions his observations on almost every page), he was the founder of a new branch of astronomy, ' Stellar Spectroscopy,' and his analysis was so comprehensive and so thorough that Secchi's types of stellar spectra will ever remain an essential illustration in astronomical text-books."   Here we have quoted once more from Father Rigge's article.

[11] This is the catalogue, in nine quarto volumes, of the works written by Jesuits during their existence for about three hundred years.

With all this it would be thought impossible that Father Secchi should ever have occupied himself with anything else. He was driven out of Rome by the Revolution of 1848, and for some two years worked at Georgetown University, in Washington, D. C. There he occupied himself for a time with a study of electricity, and his first book, *Researches on Electrical Rheometry,* was accepted for publication by the Smithsonian Institute in September, 1850, and appeared as Volume III., Article II. of *Smithsonian Contributions to Knowledge,* Washington, 1852. His observations in electricity naturally led him to magnetism, and he was one of the first to build a magnetic observatory and record and investigate carefully the behavior of the magnetic elements of the earth. Whatever he touched he illuminated. He built a third observatory for meteorology. His ingenuity enabled him to invent a number of instruments for the automatic observation of the weather, and one of these, his meteorograph, was exhibited at the Paris Universal Exhibition of 1867 and won for its inventor the grand prize of 100,000 francs and the cross of the Legion of Honor. This distinction was conferred upon Father Secchi by the Emperor Napoleon III in person, in the presence of the Emperors of Russia and Austria and of the kings of Prussia and Belgium. The Emperor of Brazil sent him a golden rose as a token of his appreciation.

We think that even this brief enumeration of

what Father Secchi accomplished will make it very clear that he was not only one of the greatest astronomers of the modern time, but also one of the acutest scientific minds of the nineteenth century. With all this he was an extremely faithful priest and a devout religious. He was noted for his faithfulness to his religious duties and for his devotion to his Order. In his first book, *L'Unita della Forze Fisiche* ("The Unity of Physical Forces"), he demonstrates the wonderful unity that obtains among the great forces of nature, and how this unity is an implied proof of the existence and oneness of the Creator. No one has penetrated more deeply into modern physical science, and no one had realized the wonders of astronomy which, through the spectroscope, have been brought into the realm of men's knowledge in the last half century; yet his science, far from creating any doubts or difficulties for his faith, had strengthened his belief in the Creator, in Providence and in the beneficence of the mysterious powers that we feel all round us.

There have been other scarcely less distinguished contributors to astronomy than Father Secchi among the Jesuits of the nineteenth century. One of the best known of these was Father de Vico, whose determination of the rotation period of Venus and the inclination of its axis was considered so exhaustive that it was not questioned for half a century. Father de Vico also measured the eccentric position of Saturn in his rings, and observed the motions of the two inner moons of this planet, which had not been seen before this time, except by Herschel. He also discovered eight comets, one of them being the well-known comet with a period of five and a half years, which bears his name. Unfortunately this devoted observer, who had already given such magnificent evidence of his power to help in the development of astronomy, was driven from Rome during the Revolution of 1848 and went first to France, where he was enthusiastically welcomed by Arago, and then to England, whence he came to Georgetown College, but after a few months· died, at the early age of forty-three.

Father Perry, of Stonyhurst College, England, was another of the distinguished Jesuit astronomers of the nineteenth century whose observations made him known to all the astronomical world. On a number of occasions he was asked to head astronomical expeditions sent out by the British government to do special work. He was in command of the expedition to Kerguelen Land in 1874 to observe the transit of Venus in the South Indian Ocean. At the next transit of Venus, in 1882, Father Perry was asked to head another expedition which made its observations in Madagascar. At least four times he went at the head of expeditions to observe total eclipses of the sun. In 1889 he headed the expedition for this purpose that had its headquarters near Devil's Island, in the West

Indies, since made famous by the Dreyfus case, and here he died of a pestilential fever, after having accomplished some of the best work done anywhere during this eclipse. Father Perry was noted for his observations on Jupiter's satellites and for having done excellent work in meteorology and magnetic surveying, as well as establishing routine work of great value at Stonyhurst. His observations on sun-spots conducted there was particularly valuable.

Father Sidgreaves, who succeeded Father Perry as the director of the Stonyhurst College Observatory, is doing photographic work in astronomy that has attracted wide-spread attention. His photographs of the spectra of new stars and of the changing spectra of certain stars were exhibited at the Royal Society of England and the Paris Exposition, and attracted much attention. Father Hagan, of the Georgetown University, is known for his work on variable stars and his *Atlas of Variable Stars* has laid a definite foundation of knowledge in this important subject which enables astronomers to carry their observations further with absolute assurance of progress. Father Algue, of Manila, is known for his work in meteorology rather than astronomy proper, but he is looked upon as the world authority on the sudden storms of the Philippines. It was he who, at the invitation of the United States Government, issued the large work in two volumes on *The Filipino Archipel-*

ago published some eight years ago by the Government Printing Office.[12]

The New Society, as the refounded Order is sometimes called, has been quite as ingenious in its inventions of instruments as the old Society. One of the problems that has bothered astronomers has been the question of the exact moment of star transits, and the difficulty that even the estimate of the same observer is subject to considerable variations. Father Baum, of the Hungarian Observatory, and Father Fargis, of Georgetown University, have each of them suggested methods of overcoming this difficulty by instrumental means. Father Fargis has eliminated the personal equation in transit observation by a photographic process. His method is an improvement upon the one with which Professors Pickering and Bigelow had been experimenting at Harvard, and it seems to solve the difficulty. Father Algue, of Manila, who was at Georgetown for some time, has invented a modification of this which promises much. Father Braun suggested the invention of the spectroheliograph for photographing the whole sun, with its spots and prominences. Father de Vico invented an instrumental device praised by Arago, enabling observers to see the internal

[12] *L'Archipielago Filipino.* Por Algunos Padres de la Mision de la Compania de Jesus en estas islas. Two volumes. Washington: Government Printing Office, 1900.

satellites of Saturn in telescopes much smaller than the one used by Herschel.

The literary activity of the new Society has been quite up to the standard set by the old Society. We have already called attention to the almost incredible labors of Father Secchi, but other great works deserve to be mentioned. Father Hagen's *Atlas of Variable Stars* is highly appreciated by astronomers everywhere, while his *Synopsis of the Higher Mathematics,* in four volumes quarto, has a great reputation in the mathematical world. There has been a stamp of scholarliness in Jesuit astronomical work that has attracted wide-spread attention. Fathers Strassmeier and Epping, working together, the one as an Assyriologist, the other as an astrologer, upon Babylonian bricks containing astronomical data, have shown that the Babylonians knew even more about scientific astronomy than we were inclined to attribute to them. Father Kugler, of Alkenberg, in Holland, has added to this. Father Karl Braun, of Mariaschein, Bohemia, has written books upon gravity and cosmogony that deserve even more attention than they have received, though they have been the subject of high praise from those who are best fitted to judge of their significance.

The Popes have always been interested in astronomy, and though the invasion of Rome by the present Italian Government deprived them of their revenues as rulers and made them dependent on the alms of Christendom, just as soon as the Roman Pontiffs felt themselves in the position to encourage science without its interfering with their fulfilment of absolutely essential religious matters, the question of having a special Papal Observatory, such as had been the custom for centuries, came to them, and was considered to be one of the duties just next to that of the care for Christianity itself. After thinking of it for some years and planning how it could be accomplished, Pope Leo XIII in 1887 established the Vatican Observatory, and appointed as its first director Father Denza, a Barnabite. This was in 1887, and Father Denza continued to do good work, especially in the organization of the observatory, until 1894 when he was succeeded by Father Angelo Rodriguez, a Dominican. These two distinguished observers devoted themselves mainly to meteorology, however, since with their imperfect equipment they would thus be able to accomplish much more that was of practical and scientific value. They published many papers on various subjects, and Father Rodriguez developed the observatory's work to such an extent that seven assistants were required.

It was felt, however, that greater devotion to astronomy as a pure science would be more desirable for the work of the Vatican Observatory, so at Father Rodriguez's death in 1906 Father Hagen, who had been for some years in charge of the Observatory of Georgetown University, Washington, D. C., was summoned to Rome to be the Director of the Vatican Observatory. He had done, even early in his career, some magnificent work, despite limited opportunities and cramped facilities, and had shown himself to be a distinguished astronomical genius amid many drawbacks. His work for science constitutes one of those romances of modern science that should be better known, because they serve to show that it is not opportunity nor external circumstances that count but the man, his capacity for work, and his powers of observation. Father Hagen was born 6 March, 1887, at Bregenz in the Tyrol, and made his studies at Feldkirch in Austria. He entered the Society of Jesus at sixteen years of age and took a special course of studies at Münster and Bonn, at both of which Universities his professor was Edward Heis, the distinguished German Catholic astronomer, whose work on the variable stars, on the Milky Way, on meteoric swarms, and the zodiacal light deservedly brought him such wide recognition in the nineteenth century. Father Hagen was ordained to the priesthood, 25 February, 1878. This was the day before Father Secchi's death.

After his ordination he was sent to the United States to teach, and was stationed for nearly ten years in the 'eighties at Prairie du Chien, Wisconsin. His principal occupation was teaching mathematics and the sciences, and none of those around him had any idea of the genius of the man. In spite of many discouragements he took up the study of astronomy and mounted a three-

inch telescope on gas pipes, having secured,
though only with some difficulty, a small shed in
which to house it. He had only a limited amount
of time at his disposal for astronomical observations, and he took up the study of the variable
stars. It was not long before his observations
began to attract attention, and notwithstanding
the poverty of his astronomical outfit he did
some good work. In 1888 he was summoned
back to Germany, and was already on his way
home when Father Richards, S.J., President of
Georgetown University who was looking for a
head for the Observatory there asked and obtained permission for Fr. Hagen to stay and become the Director. In the course of the next ten
years Father Hagen's work made him known
throughout the astronomical world. When he
was summoned to Rome to become the Director
at the Vatican it was felt everywhere that no
better choice than this could have been made.
From him we may look confidently in the not
distant future for another important chapter in
astronomy as illuminated by Jesuits.

For those who know anything about this marvelous activity of the great Jesuit Order in astronomical matters it is impossible to understand
how any intelligent person with such data before
him should continue to express the opinion that
the Church has been opposed to the development
of science, and, above all, astronomical science.
The Jesuits are thoroughly representative of
what is usually thought to be the most conser-

vative element in the Church. They have been
universally conceded to represent the mind of
the Popes as closely as is possible. They are directly under the orders of the Pope, singly and
as a body. If there was any tendency to discourage the development of astronomy, they would
never have taken it up originally, and they surely
would not have been allowed to devote so much
time and so many of their most promising men
to it for nearly three centuries. They began their
work in astronomy nearly a century before the
Galileo case. They were extremely active in it
during the time when Galileo is supposed to have
been so much persecuted. They continued their
activity afterward and have kept it up even to
the present day. Their success is the pride of
their own Order, and is looked upon as a bright
jewel in the Church's crown by ecclesiastical
authorities.

Those who think the Galileo incident so significant must either be ignorant of all this real
history of astronomy or else they must have explained it away to their satisfaction as one of
these pretenses which is supposed to be expressed by the word Jesuitism. If a pretense of
interest in science can enable men to accomplish
as much of absolute scientific value as the Jesuits
have done in astronomy, then what we want is
more of such pretense and a lot more of these
pretenders. Meantime, the only conclusion must
be that the story of what the Jesuits have done
in astronomy before and after Galileo is the com-

plete contradiction of what is so often written, with regard to the Church's opposition to science as exemplified by the Galileo case, by those who are unacquainted with the wonderful chapter in the history of astronomy by the Church's most faithful sons.

INDEX.

(223)